Secondary Sources

Encyclopedia
Words and Phrases
Textbooks
Treatises
Practitioner's Handbooks
Loose Leaf Services
Legal Dictionaries
Citation Books
Legal Thesauruses
Law Reviews
WESTLAW

Finding Tools

Digests

American Digest System

Century Digest	1658 to 1896
First Decennial Digest	1897 to 1906
Second Decennial Digest	1907 to 1916
Third Decennial Digest	1916 to 1926
Fourth Decennial Digest	1926 to 1936
Fifth Decennial Digest	1936 to 1946
Sixth Decennial Digest	1946 to 1956
Seventh Decennial Digest	1956 to 1966
Eighth Decennial Digest	1966 to 1976
Ninth Decennial Digest, Part I	1976 to 1981
Ninth Decennial Digest, Part II	1981 to 1986
Tenth Decennial Digest, Part I	1986 to 1991
Tenth Decennial Digest, Part II	1991 to 1996
General Digest	1996 to Present

Other Digests

Supreme Court Digest
Federal Practice Digest
State and Reporter Digests
Selected Case Series Digests
Subject or Special Reports Digest
WESTLAW

Tables of

Cases Reported
Cases Digested, Plaintiff
Cases Digested, Defendant
Cases Affirmed, Reversed, or Modified
Cases Cited by Popular Name
Cases Cited
Parallel Citations
Statutes Construed

Other

Indexes to Legal Periodicals

Computer Assisted Legal Research

WESTLAW

Contents

Outline of Legal Reference Material
Introduction
How to Analyze Facts

Introduction

This workbook provides pages from major West publications and screens from WESTLAW, along with problems to illustrate the use of these research tools.

If this is your first experience with legal research, the following pages provide you with helpful information.

"How to Analyze Fact Situations" is a suggested framework for you to use to analyze facts and isolate words or concepts important to your research.

The Outline of Legal Reference Material indicates the organization of reference sources into three main categories. They are: **Primary Sources**--materials containing the text of the law such as cases from federal or state courts or statutes passed by legislatures, **Secondary Sources**--books such as encyclopedias, dictionaries and treatises which explain and comment on the law and **Finding Tools**--such as digests which help you find material pertinent to your research problem.

WESTLAW, our computer assisted legal research service, can act as a primary, secondary or finding source, depending on how it is used.

When you research legal issues you are often confronted with a multitude of facts but minimal direction. In order to successfully complete your research you need to sift through the facts and concepts and decide which are most important to your research. The technique suggested below is one many researchers use successfully. It can be used for the sample problems in the chapters on Digests, USCA, and Am Jur 2d. A similar technique can also be used for WESTLAW research.

West Digests

The Digest chapter illustrates the use of West's indexing system to find cases dealing with your legal issue. You will use the important words from your worksheet, consult the descriptive-word index and find key numbers which lead you to digests of case law.

Digest Problem

Government agents observed a person buying chemicals which could be used to make an illegal drug. Without a warrant, they placed a wiretap on the suspect's phone line, and as a result, discovered the location of the warehouse where the illegal drug is made. They then made an arrest at the warehouse. The attorney for the defense wishes to make a motion to exclude evidence seized as a result of the placement of the wiretap without a warrant. What case law discusses the unauthorized use of wiretaps?

Worksheet

Parties:

Places and Things:

Basis of Action or Issue:

Defense:

Relief Sought:

WEST'S

FEDERAL PRACTICE

DIGEST 4th

Volume 99

DESCRIPTIVE – WORD INDEX

P — Z

ST. PAUL, MINN.

WEST PUBLISHING CO.

WINDING UP
DISSOLUTION, generally, see this index Dissolution

WINDOW WASHERS
INJURIES, master's liability. Emp Liab 51
WORKERS' compensation. Work Comp 146

WINDOWS
ADJOINING landowner's right to construct. Adj Land 10(2)

WIRE FRAUD
See this index Telegraphs and Telephones

WIRELESS COMMUNICATIONS
See generally, this index Television and Radio

WIRES
AUTOMOBILES, injuries from wires obstructing highway. Autos 265
COMPENSATION for occupation of highways with wires. Em Dom 119(6)
ELECTRICITY, generally, see this index Electricity
STREETS—
    Power of city to grant right to place wires in streets. Mun Corp 680(5)
TELEGRAPHS and telephones, generally, see this index Telegraphs and Telephones

WIRETAPPING
Generally. Tel 493–530
EVIDENCE in criminal prosecutions. Crim Law 394.3
FEDERAL preemption—
    State laws or regulations. States 18.81
INTERCEPTION or disclosure of communications, generally, see this index Telecommunications
PRESUMPTIONS—
    Consent. Tel 495
TERRITORIAL constitutional prohibition—
    Federal laws, effect on. Territories 18
TRANSCRIPTS—
    Expungement. Tel 527
WRONGFULLY obtained information—
    Admissibility. Evid 154

WISCONSIN
PUBLIC lands. Pub Lands 187

WISDOM
ADMINISTRATIVE law and procedure, see this index Administrative Law and Procedure
MUNICIPAL corporations, judicial supervision where wisdom of action is involved. Mun Corp 63.1(3)

WISH
BARGAINING units, desires of employees. Labor 203

WITHDRAWAL
ACCESSORY before the fact. Crim Law 73
ACTION—
    Conclusiveness of judgment. Judgm 590(5)
ADOPTION, withdrawal of consent, effect. Adop 7.6
AFFIDAVIT or information in contempt proceedings. Contempt 54(7)
APPEAL or other proceedings for review—
    App & E 14(1), 776
    Fed Cts 721
    Justices' court. J P 166
    Workers' compensation, proceedings to secure compensation. Work Comp 1908
APPEARANCE, see this index Appearance
ATTORNEY and client—
    Generally, see this index Attorney and Client
BETS. Gaming 24, 29

WITHDRAWAL—Cont'd
BIDS—
    Public improvements. Mun Corp 335(1)
BUILDING and loan associations, see this index Building and Loan Associations
CANDIDATE for office. Elections 174
CASE or question from jury—
    Crim Law 750
    Trial 134–181
CHALLENGES to jury. Jury 110(15)
COMMINGLED funds of trust and individual, withdrawals from. Trusts 358(2)
CONSENT to petition or other application for public improvements. Mun Corp 292(5)
CONSPIRACY. Consp 40.4
COUNTS, questions for jury. Trial 145
CREATION of trust of deposits in bank as affected by subsequent withdrawals. Trusts 34(4)
DEFAULT judgment, see this index Default Judgment
DEMISED premises from rental market affecting recovery of premises under law suspending remedy. Land & Ten 278.7(8)
DEMURRER. Equity 238
DUE process of law. Const Law 307
DUTIABLE goods from bond. Cust Dut 91
ELECTIONS, see this index Elections
EMPLOYMENT, labor disputes and concerted activities, see this index Labor Disputes and Concerted Activities
ERROR in admission of evidence cured by withdrawal. Homic 338(4)
ESTATE from administration. Ex & Ad 7
EVIDENCE—
    Crim Law 677
    Trial 58
    Error cured by withdrawal—
        App & E 1053(1, 2)
        Crim Law 1169.5
    Instructions, application to evidence. Trial 252(3)
    Review of rulings. App & E 1047(3)
EXCEPTIONS to pleading. Equity 255½
EXECUTION—
    See this index Execution in Judicial Proceedings
FORMER action, conclusiveness of judgment. Judgm 590(5)
FUNDS deposited in court. Dep in Court 10
GARNISHMENT. Garn 197
HARMLESS error, see this index Harmless Error
INTERROGATORIES to jury. Trial 354
JUDGMENT—
    By confession on withdrawal of plea. Judgm 55
    Default judgment, see this index Default Judgment
    Offer of judgment. Judgm 80
JURY—
    Crim Law 750, 751
    Trial 146
    Challenges to juror. Jury 110(15)
    Waiver of jury trial, see this index Jury
LABOR disputes and concerted activities, see this index Labor Disputes and Concerted Activities
MEMBERS—
    Associations. Assoc 9
    Beneficial associations. Ben Assoc 9
    Labor organizations. Labor 105
MOTIONS. Motions 35
NAMES from liquor license application. Int Liq 66(9), 68(7)
NOMINEE. Elections 146
OFFER—
    Contract. Contracts 19
    Judgment. Judgm 80
    To buy. Sales 23(2)
    To sell. Sales 22(2)
PARTIES, effect as to competency as witness. Witn 139(4)
PARTNER, see this index Partnership

WEST'S
FEDERAL PRACTICE
DIGEST 4th

Volume 28B

CRIMINAL LAW ⊙═ 372 to 397

ST. PAUL, MN

WEST GROUP

CRIMINAL LAW

SUBJECTS INCLUDED

Acts and omissions in violation of law punishable as offenses against the public

Nature and elements of crime in general

Capacity to commit crime, nature and extent of responsibility therefore in general, and responsibility of principals, accessories, etc.

Jurisdiction over and place of prosecution of crimes

Limitation of time for prosecution

Preliminary complaints, warrants, examination and commitment

Arraignment and pleas

Evidence in criminal proceedings

Trial, and acquittal or conviction

Motions in arrest of judgment and for new trial

Judgment or sentence and final commitment

Review on appeal, writ of error or certiorari

Prosecution and punishment of successive offenses or of habitual criminals

Modes of punishment and prevention of crime in general

SUBJECTS EXCLUDED AND COVERED BY OTHER TOPICS

Arrest, see ARREST

Bail, see BAIL

Constitutional rights and privileges of accused not peculiar to matters within scope of this topic, see CONSTITUTIONAL LAW, INDICTMENT AND INFORMATION, JURY, SEARCHES AND SEIZURES, WITNESSES and other specific topics

Convicts, disabilities and regulation, see CONVICTS

Costs in criminal prosecutions, see COSTS

Extradition of fugitives, see EXTRADITION AND DETAINERS

Fines in general, see FINES

Grand juries and inquisitions by them, see GRAND JURY

Habeas corpus to obtain discharge from imprisonment, see HABEAS CORPUS

Included offenses, conviction under indictment for broader offense, see INDICTMENT AND INFORMATION

Indictments or other accusations, see INDICTMENT AND INFORMATION and specific topics relating to particular offenses

Injunction against commission of crime, see INJUNCTION

Judgment of acquittal, conviction or sentence, effect as adjudication, see JUDGMENT

Jury trial, right to and waiver, and qualifications and selection of jurors, see JURY

Juvenile offenders, special rules and proceedings, see INFANTS

Military offenses and court-martial prosecutions, see ARMED SERVICES, MILITARY JUSTICE

Pardon, commutation of sentence, and parole, see PARDON AND PAROLE

Particular classes of persons, criminal responsibility, see INFANTS, MENTAL HEALTH and other specific topics

Particular offenses, substantive and procedural questions peculiar to, see HOMICIDE, LARCENY and other specific topics

Pecuniary punishment and deprivation of property as punishment for violation of law, see FORFEITURES, PENALTIES, INTOXICATING LIQUORS and other specific topics

Prisons and reformatories, establishment and regulation, see PRISONS, INFANTS, IX

Prosecuting attorneys, see DISTRICT AND PROSECUTING ATTORNEYS

Searches and seizures, see ARREST, SEARCHES AND SEIZURES, INTOXICATING LIQUORS and other specific topics

Witnesses and their examination, see WITNESSES

For detailed references to other topics, see Descriptive-Word Index

---

Analysis

after Coast Guard tracked the vessel by use of the transmitter. U.S.C.A. Const.Amend. 4.

> U.S. v. Juda, 46 F.3d 961, certiorari denied Paris v. U.S., 115 S.Ct. 1811, 514 U.S. 1090, 131 L.Ed.2d 735, certiorari denied 115 S.Ct. 2632, 515 U.S. 1169, 132 L.Ed.2d 872.

C.A.9 (Cal.) 1991. Even if omission of statements from affidavit in support of wiretap was product of bad faith conduct by law enforcement officials, evidence seized as result of wiretap did not have to be suppressed, where additional or omitted material would not have eliminated probable cause. U.S.C.A. Const. Amend. 4.

> U.S. v. Tham, 960 F.2d 1391.

C.A.9 (Cal.) 1987. If the full details about the informant's penetration into defendant's activities were known to judge, who authorized FBI wiretaps of defendant's home telephone and several public telephones defendant regularly used, reasonable district court judge would have denied the application because necessity for wiretap order had not been shown, and the specific facts withheld from the judge about the investigation revealed that traditional techniques could have led to successful infiltration of defendant's entire enterprise; therefore, evidence obtained from the wiretaps had to be suppressed. 18 U.S.C.A. § 2518.

> U.S. v. Simpson, 813 F.2d 1462, certiorari denied 108 S.Ct. 233, 484 U.S. 898, 98 L.Ed.2d 192, certiorari denied Anderson v. U.S., 108 S.Ct. 233, 484 U.S. 898, 98 L.Ed.2d 192, appeal after remand 927 F.2d 1088.

C.A.9 (Cal.) 1987. Even if Philippine wiretap was illegal under Philippine law, reliance on wiretap's legality by United States authorities participating in joint narcotics investigation was objectively reasonable where federal officers sought, and received, assurances from high ranking Philippine law enforcement authorities that all necessary authorization was being obtained, and thus evidence seized on basis of wiretap information was admissible under good-faith exception to exclusionary rule. U.S.C.A. Const.Amend. 4.

> U.S. v. Peterson, 812 F.2d 486.

C.A.9 (Cal.) 1985. Reasoning of the *Franks* decision, which governs suppression of evidence seized pursuant to a search warrant that has been issued on basis of an affidavit containing material false statements concerning probable cause, applies as well to wiretap orders. 18 U.S.C.A. § 2518.

> U.S. v. Ippolito, 774 F.2d 1482.

The "necessity" required for a wiretap authorization is material to issuance of a wiretap order and is subject to the *Franks* rule governing suppression of evidence derived from wiretap authorization issued on basis of an affidavit that contains false statements. 18 U.S.C.A. § 2518(1)(c), (3)(c).

> U.S. v. Ippolito, 774 F.2d 1482.

In determining whether information gained through wiretap should be suppressed because of a *Franks* violation, an appropriate approach is to delete false or misleading statements in wiretap request and to insert the omitted truths revealed at the suppression hearing. 18 U.S.C.A. § 2518.

> U.S. v. Ippolito, 774 F.2d 1482.

False and misleading information in Government affidavits concerning necessity of wiretaps required suppression of information derived from the wiretaps; Government's misleading the issuing judge about willingness of a particular informant to testify and his ability to uncover evidence of conspiracy using only conventional techniques involved a material element for wiretap authorization, to wit, necessity, and warrant was insufficient where the misleading matter was deleted and the revelations at suppression hearing concerning informant's willingness to testify and ability to penetrate drug organization inserted. 18 U.S.C.A. § 2518.

> U.S. v. Ippolito, 774 F.2d 1482.

C.A.9 (Cal.) 1984. Tape recordings of conversation between Internal Revenue Service undercover agents and defendants were lawful and admissible under federal law, although defendants contended that tape recording violated California statute prohibiting electronic eavesdropping without consent of all parties to communication. 18 U.S.C.A. § 371; West's Ann.Cal.Penal Code § 632.

> U.S. v. Little, 753 F.2d 1420.

Undercover Internal Revenue Service agent was not under an affirmative duty to respond truthfully when questioned about his or her true identity; thus, tapes of conversations between defendants and IRS agent were not subject to suppression on the basis that they were secured by fraud, deceit and trickery.

> U.S. v. Little, 753 F.2d 1420.

C.A.9 (Cal.) 1975. In a case where it is clear that minimization provision of a wiretap order was disregarded by Government throughout period covered by order, a total suppression might well be appropriate, but where district court finds reasonable and good-faith efforts on part of Government to comply with order, such suppression is not required. 18 U.S.C.A. § 2518(10)(a).

> U. S. v. Turner, 528 F.2d 143, certiorari denied Grimes v. U.S., 96 S.Ct. 426, 423 U.S. 996, 46 L.Ed.2d 371, certiorari denied Lewis v. U.S., 96 S.Ct. 426, 423 U.S. 996, 46 L.Ed.2d 371, certiorari denied Hackett v. U.S., 97 S.Ct. 105, 429 U.S. 837, 50 L.Ed.2d 103.

C.A.9 (Cal.) 1973. U. S. v. Chavez, 478 F.2d 512, certiorari granted 93 S.Ct. 2292, 412 U.S. 905, 36 L.Ed.2d 969, affirmed in part, reversed in part 94 S.Ct. 1849, 416 U.S. 562, 40 L.Ed.2d 380, on remand 533 F.2d 491, certiorari denied 96 S.Ct. 2237, 426 U.S. 911, 48 L.Ed.2d 837.

C.A.10 (Colo.) 1989. Unintentional failure of wiretap application to list defendant as prior interceptee in state wiretap affidavit did not require suppression of evidence; listing defendant as prior interceptee would have supported Government's application for interception order. 18 U.S.C.A. § 2518(1)(e).

> U.S. v. Pinelli, 890 F.2d 1461, certiorari denied Sheehan v. U.S., 110 S.Ct. 1498, 494 U.S. 1038, 108 L.Ed.2d 632, certiorari denied 110 S.Ct. 2568, 495 U.S. 960, 109 L.Ed.2d 750.

Four-day delay between termination of wiretap and sealing of original tapes did not require suppression of evidence; Government amply explained reasons for delay.

> U.S. v. Pinelli, 890 F.2d 1461, certiorari denied Sheehan v. U.S., 110 S.Ct. 1498, 494 U.S. 1038, 108 L.Ed.2d 632, certiorari denied 110 S.Ct. 2568, 495 U.S. 960, 109 L.Ed.2d 750.

C.A.10 (Colo.) 1986. Government's use of pen register on telephone without warrant, in violation of state constitutional standards, did not so taint search warrant authorizing tapping of telephone as to require suppression of evidence attributable to tap; although FBI agent testified that information gleaned from pen register had been used in preparing affidavit for warrant, that information was only small part of probable cause showing, and affidavit was based for the most part on reliable informants' tips and results of police surveillance. U.S.C.A. Const.Amend. 4.

> U.S. v. Cook, 794 F.2d 561, certiorari denied 107 S.Ct. 288, 479 U.S. 889, 93 L.Ed.2d 262.

C.A.10 (Colo.) 1985. Evidence derived from Canadian wiretaps, conducted pursuant to Canada's less restrictive wiretap law, was admissible, where conduct of Canadian police officers did not "shock the judicial conscience," and participation of American officers in the investigation did not give rise to a joint venture. U.S.C.A. Const.Amend. 4; 18 U.S.C.A. §§ 2510 et seq., 2518(a).

> U.S. v. Delaplane, 778 F.2d 570, certiorari denied 107 S.Ct. 104, 479 U.S. 827, 93 L.Ed.2d 54.

Wiretapped telephone conversation between unidentified male and unidentified female, made in connection with drug investigation, in which female explained "Michael's back," was admissible under Rule 803 as evidence of identity of one of the defendants. Fed.Rules Evid.Rule 803, 28 U.S.C.A.

> U.S. v. Delaplane, 778 F.2d 570, certiorari denied 107 S.Ct. 104, 479 U.S. 827, 93 L.Ed.2d 54.

C.A.2 (Conn.) 1993. Under the *Franks* standard, government's failure to disclose information that conversations it wanted to intercept would occur at particular location did not require suppression of conversations intercepted pursuant to "roving bug" order; information concerning address was not essential for permitting interceptions, because there was enough independent information of nature of crimes and evasive methods of suspects to justify roving bug order; moreover, even if judge had been advised of particular address, information would not have eliminated need for roving order, because suspects were trying to avoid detection, and could easily have changed location at the last minute. U.S.C.A. Const.Amend. 4; 18 U.S.C.A. § 2518(1)(b), (3)(a, b, d), (4), (11)(a).

> U.S. v. Bianco, 998 F.2d 1112, certiorari denied 114 S.Ct. 1644, 511 U.S. 1069, 128 L.Ed.2d 364.

Government violated wiretap statute in application for warrant to conduct roving electronic surveillance of alleged members of organized crime family by failing to disclose prior applications for electronic surveillance of suspects who were not targets of "roving bug" request but who were mentioned in supporting affidavit; however, violation did not require suppression of evidence obtained pursuant to "roving bug" warrant, where government believed that it was necessary to disclose prior applications concerning only proposed targets of "roving bug," and thus omission of prior surveillance applications was not intentional, but inadvertent. 18 U.S.C.A. § 2518(1)(e), (11)(a).

> U.S. v. Bianco, 998 F.2d 1112, certiorari denied 114 S.Ct. 1644, 511 U.S. 1069, 128 L.Ed.2d 364.

C.A.2 (Conn.) 1990. If surveillance tapes have not been sealed immediately, they must be suppressed unless the Government furnishes an explanation for the delay that is satisfactory within meaning of Omnibus Crime Control Act. 18 U.S.C.A. § 2518(8)(a).

> U.S. v. Maldonado-Rivera, 922 F.2d 934, certiorari denied Ramirez-Talavera v. U.S., 111 S.Ct. 2811, 501 U.S. 1211, 115 L.Ed.2d 984, certiorari denied Segarra-Palmer v. U.S., 111 S.Ct. 2858, 501 U.S. 1233, 115 L.Ed.2d 1025, certiorari denied 111 S.Ct. 2858, 501 U.S. 1233, 115 L.Ed.2d 1026.

Fact that "work tapes," which officers had made at the same time as tapes of intercepted conversations which were offered at trial, con-

For cited U.S.C.A. sections and legislative history, see United States Code Annotated

tained some material not on tapes offered at trial did not require suppression of the tapes offered at trial, either under the Omnibus Crime Control Act, on due process grounds, under the Jencks Act, or on the basis of Rule 16; district court found that only four of 39 work tapes had excess material, with the unauthorized material totaling 11 minutes, and that the extra material occurred as result of periodic sound checks in which agents adjusted the tape input switch on the main recorders but failed to make corresponding adjustment to cassette recorders on which the work tapes were being made. 18 U.S.C.A. §§ 2518(8)(a), 3500; Fed.Rules Cr. Proc.Rule 16, 18 U.S.C.A.; U.S.C.A. Const. Amend. 5.

> U.S. v. Maldonado-Rivera, 922 F.2d 934, certiorari denied Ramirez-Talavera v. U.S., 111 S.Ct. 2811, 501 U.S. 1211, 115 L.Ed.2d 984, certiorari denied Segarra-Palmer v. U.S., 111 S.Ct. 2858, 501 U.S. 1233, 115 L.Ed.2d 1025, certiorari denied 111 S.Ct. 2858, 501 U.S. 1233, 115 L.Ed.2d 1026.

C.A.2 (Conn.) 1989. Government failed to demonstrate satisfactory explanation for delay of up to 82 or 96 days in sealing tape recordings of intercepted telephone conversations after expiration of authorization order, mandating suppression of recordings. 18 U.S.C.A. §§ 2510 et seq., 2518(8)(a), (10)(a).

> U.S. v. Ojeda Rios, 875 F.2d 17, certiorari granted 110 S.Ct. 231, 493 U.S. 889, 107 L.Ed.2d 183, vacated 110 S.Ct. 1845, 495 U.S. 257, 109 L.Ed.2d 224.

C.A.2 (Conn.) 1987. Government's delay in sealing tape recordings obtained by legal wiretap did not render inadmissible evidence indirectly derived from wiretap, consisting of evidence seized by police in search for which taped conversations had furnished probable cause. 18 U.S.C.A. §§ 2517(2, 3), 2518(8)(a).

> U.S. v. Donlan, 825 F.2d 653.

C.A.2 (Conn.) 1987. Use of ambiguous phrase "12 a.m. to 12 p.m." in order authorizing wiretap was mere clerical error and did not warrant suppression of wiretap evidence; wiretap application and supporting affidavits unequivocally established that 24–hour interception of telephone conversations was requested, and panel of state judges that authorized wiretap subsequently indicated intent to authorize 24–hour interception.

> U.S. v. Rosario, 820 F.2d 584.

C.A.2 (Conn.) 1986. When government's presentation of tapes from wiretap has not been immediate, defendants' motion for suppression of tapes must be granted unless government's

explanation for delay in presentation is satisfactory. 18 U.S.C.A. § 2518(8)(a).

> U.S. v. Rodriguez, 786 F.2d 472, appeal after remand U.S. v. Donlan, 825 F.2d 653.

Fact that there is no evidence that tapes from wiretap have been tampered with or that delay in government's presenting tapes for judicial sealing caused defendants any prejudice does not relieve government of its burden to present satisfactory explanation for delay. 18 U.S.C.A. § 2518(8)(a).

> U.S. v. Rodriguez, 786 F.2d 472, appeal after remand U.S. v. Donlan, 825 F.2d 653.

Failure of supervising assistant to United States Attorney to get another assistant United States attorney to handle presentation of wiretap tapes earlier than was done was not unreasonable in the absence of any basis for inferring that assistant United States attorney other than supervising attorney would have had sufficient familiarity with surveillance to prepare report earlier than was done. 18 U.S.C.A. § 2518(8)(a).

> U.S. v. Rodriguez, 786 F.2d 472, appeal after remand U.S. v. Donlan, 825 F.2d 653.

C.A.3 (Del.) 1975. U. S. v. Shaffer, 520 F.2d 1369, certiorari denied Vespe v. U.S., 96 S.Ct. 779, 423 U.S. 1051, 46 L.Ed.2d 640.

C.A.11 (Fla.) 1997. That recorded cordless telephone conversations were allegedly obtained in violation of state law did not prevent their admission in federal prosecution.

> U.S. v. Brazel, 102 F.3d 1120, certiorari denied Jefferson v. U.S., 118 S.Ct. 78, 139 L.Ed.2d 37, certiorari denied Archer v. U.S., 118 S.Ct. 78, 139 L.Ed.2d 37, certiorari denied McNealy v. U.S., 118 S.Ct. 78, 139 L.Ed.2d 37, certiorari denied 118 S.Ct. 79, 139 L.Ed.2d 37, certiorari denied Burgess v. U.S., 118 S.Ct. 720.

Federal law governs admissibility of tape recordings in federal criminal cases, and complaints that evidence was obtained in violation of state law are of no effect.

> U.S. v. Brazel, 102 F.3d 1120, certiorari denied Jefferson v. U.S., 118 S.Ct. 78, 139 L.Ed.2d 37, certiorari denied Archer v. U.S., 118 S.Ct. 78, 139 L.Ed.2d 37, certiorari denied McNealy v. U.S., 118 S.Ct. 78, 139 L.Ed.2d 37, certiorari denied 118 S.Ct. 79, 139 L.Ed.2d 37, certiorari denied Burgess v. U.S., 118 S.Ct. 720.

C.A.11 (Fla.) 1987. Wiretap evidence was not inadmissible because application for wiretap order failed to affirmatively demonstrate absence of assistant Attorney General for Criminal Division from District of Columbia at time authorization was made; authorization by assistant Attorney General of Tax Division was presumably valid, and evidence at suppression hearing had established that absence. 18 U.S.C.A. § 2516.

U.S. v. Weber, 808 F.2d 1422.

Wiretap evidence was admissible even if special agent's allegedly contradictory statements and separate affidavits in support of wiretap order were fraudulent; despite any presumed deficiency in affidavit, wire communications were legally obtained.

U.S. v. Weber, 808 F.2d 1422.

C.A.11 (Fla.) 1986. Suppression is not mandated by inadvertent noncompliance with Title III requirement that prior applications for electronic surveillance be disclosed. 18 U.S.C.A. § 2518(1)(e).

U.S. v. Van Horn, 789 F.2d 1492, certiorari denied 107 S.Ct. 190, 479 U.S. 854, 93 L.Ed.2d 123, certiorari denied Harvey v. U.S., 107 S.Ct. 192, 479 U.S. 855, 93 L.Ed.2d 124, certiorari denied Sikes v. U.S., 107 S.Ct. 279, 479 U.S. 886, 93 L.Ed.2d 255.

No special approval is required before submission, to state courts, of application to use state evidence under section of Title III providing for judicial approval for use of evidence obtained through a state wiretap. 18 U.S.C.A. §§ 2510–2520, 2517(5).

U.S. v. Van Horn, 789 F.2d 1492, certiorari denied 107 S.Ct. 190, 479 U.S. 854, 93 L.Ed.2d 123, certiorari denied Harvey v. U.S., 107 S.Ct. 192, 479 U.S. 855, 93 L.Ed.2d 124, certiorari denied Sikes v. U.S., 107 S.Ct. 279, 479 U.S. 886, 93 L.Ed.2d 255.

State judge, in authorizing federal agents to use evidence obtained through state wiretap, complied with section of Title III requiring judicial approval, as state judge expressly found that interceptions related to federal charges were "intercepted incidentally," and, as same judge who had authorized state wiretap, was in a position to know whether state agents had properly executed state wiretap. 18 U.S.C.A. §§ 2510–2520, 2517(5).

U.S. v. Van Horn, 789 F.2d 1492, certiorari denied 107 S.Ct. 190, 479 U.S. 854, 93 L.Ed.2d 123, certiorari denied Harvey v. U.S., 107 S.Ct. 192, 479 U.S. 855, 93 L.Ed.2d 124, certiorari denied Sikes v. U.S., 107 S.Ct. 279, 479 U.S. 886, 93 L.Ed.2d 255.

Delay of five months by federal agents in requesting state judge to authorize their use of evidence obtained through state wiretap was timely under Title III section. 18 U.S.C.A. § 2517(5).

U.S. v. Van Horn, 789 F.2d 1492, certiorari denied 107 S.Ct. 190, 479 U.S. 854, 93 L.Ed.2d 123, certiorari denied Harvey v. U.S., 107 S.Ct. 192, 479 U.S. 855, 93 L.Ed.2d 124, certiorari denied Sikes v. U.S., 107 S.Ct. 279, 479 U.S. 886, 93 L.Ed.2d 255.

Use of testimony of witness implicated in state evidence used to obtain federal indictment against defendant did not violate Title III section requiring judicial approval of use of state wiretap evidence, as his testimony came from personal knowledge rather than from a surveillance. 18 U.S.C.A. §§ 2510–2520, 2517(3), (5).

U.S. v. Van Horn, 789 F.2d 1492, certiorari denied 107 S.Ct. 190, 479 U.S. 854, 93 L.Ed.2d 123, certiorari denied Harvey v. U.S., 107 S.Ct. 192, 479 U.S. 855, 93 L.Ed.2d 124, certiorari denied Sikes v. U.S., 107 S.Ct. 279, 479 U.S. 886, 93 L.Ed.2d 255.

State circuit judge was authorized, under Florida law and thus under Title III, to approve federal agents' use of state wiretap evidence. 18 U.S.C.A. §§ 2510–2520, 2510(9)(b), 2517(5); West's F.S.A. § 934.02(8).

U.S. v. Van Horn, 789 F.2d 1492, certiorari denied 107 S.Ct. 190, 479 U.S. 854, 93 L.Ed.2d 123, certiorari denied Harvey v. U.S., 107 S.Ct. 192, 479 U.S. 855, 93 L.Ed.2d 124, certiorari denied Sikes v. U.S., 107 S.Ct. 279, 479 U.S. 886, 93 L.Ed.2d 255.

Conversations of defendant's coconspirators regarding his arrest were not the product of that illegal arrest, and thus wiretap evidence of the conversations about the arrest was admissible, as causal connection between arrest and statements was broken by intervening acts of third parties.

U.S. v. Van Horn, 789 F.2d 1492, certiorari denied 107 S.Ct. 190, 479 U.S. 854, 93 L.Ed.2d 123, certiorari denied Harvey v. U.S., 107 S.Ct. 192, 479 U.S. 855, 93 L.Ed.2d 124, certiorari denied Sikes v. U.S., 107 S.Ct. 279, 479 U.S. 886, 93 L.Ed.2d 255.

C.A.5 (Fla.) 1980. U. S. v. Middlebrooks, 618 F.2d 273, opinion modified on rehearing 624 F.2d 36, certiorari denied 101 S.Ct. 401, 449 U.S. 984, 66 L.Ed.2d 246.

C.A.5 (Fla.) 1975. Government's failure to identify in electronic surveillance application person other than individual who was target of criminal investigation, despite fact that Government knew that that person's conversations would likely be intercepted, was not evidence of Government's bad faith requiring suppression of intercepted conversations as against that person, in view of fact that government attorney

For cited U.S.C.A. sections and legislative history, see United States Code Annotated

believed in good faith that such identification was not statutorily required. 18 U.S.C.A. § 2518.

> U. S. v. Kilgore, 524 F.2d 957.

C.A.11 (Ga.) 1991. Information obtained from pen register placed on a telephone can be used as evidence in a criminal trial even if court order authorizing its installation does not comply with statutory requirements; installation of pen register is not search under Fourth Amendment and does not warrant invocation of exclusionary rule. U.S.C.A. Const.Amend. 4; 18 U.S.C.A. §§ 2510 et seq., 3121 et seq.

> U.S. v. Thompson, 936 F.2d 1249, certiorari denied 112 S.Ct. 975, 502 U.S. 1075, 117 L.Ed.2d 139.

Absent specific reference to an exclusionary rule in statute regulating pen registers, violation of the statute does not require that evidence be excluded. 18 U.S.C.A. § 3121(c).

> U.S. v. Thompson, 936 F.2d 1249, certiorari denied 112 S.Ct. 975, 502 U.S. 1075, 117 L.Ed.2d 139.

C.A.11 (Ga.) 1990. Admission of recorded conversations between defendant and consenting government informant does not violate Fourth Amendment right of the accused. U.S.C.A. Const.Amend. 4.

> U.S. v. Smith, 918 F.2d 1551, rehearing denied 929 F.2d 704.

C.A.5 (Ga.) 1975. U. S. v. Howell, 514 F.2d 710, certiorari denied Harris v. U.S., 96 S.Ct. 220, 423 U.S. 914, 46 L.Ed.2d 143, certiorari denied 96 S.Ct. 220, 423 U.S. 914, 46 L.Ed.2d 143, certiorari denied Patrick v. U.S., 96 S.Ct. 220, 423 U.S. 914, 46 L.Ed.2d 143, certiorari denied Allen v. U.S., 96 S.Ct. 396, 423 U.S. 987, 46 L.Ed.2d 304, rehearing denied 527 F.2d 1373, certiorari denied 97 S.Ct. 109, 429 U.S. 838, 50 L.Ed.2d 105.

C.A.5 (Ga.) 1975. U. S. v. Doolittle, 507 F.2d 1368, on reconsideration 518 F.2d 500, certiorari denied Anderson v. U.S., 97 S.Ct. 1172, 430 U.S. 905, 51 L.Ed.2d 580, certiorari denied Malloway v. U.S., 97 S.Ct. 1173, 430 U.S. 905, 51 L.Ed.2d 580, certiorari denied 97 S.Ct. 1173, 430 U.S. 905, 51 L.Ed.2d 580, certiorari dismissed 96 S.Ct. 439, 423 U.S. 1008, 46 L.Ed.2d 380.

C.A.9 (Idaho) 1993. Statute regulating electronic surveillance by state officers prohibits introduction of electronic surveillance evidence in federal court where state standards are violated. 18 U.S.C.A. § 2516(2).

> U.S. v. Butz, 982 F.2d 1378, certiorari denied 114 S.Ct. 250, 510 U.S. 891, 126 L.Ed.2d 203.

Information obtained from wiretaps, after pen registers obtained by state officials helped to establish probable cause for wiretaps, was admissible, even though state officials did not show probable cause in application for pen registers and state law later required such showing; when pen registers were ordered, state officers were relying in good faith on existing state law, which did not require showing of probable cause, and thus good-faith exception to exclusionary rule applied. Idaho Const. Art. 1, § 17; U.S.C.A. Const.Amend. 4; I.C. §§ 18–6719 to 18–6725.

> U.S. v. Butz, 982 F.2d 1378, certiorari denied 114 S.Ct. 250, 510 U.S. 891, 126 L.Ed.2d 203.

C.A.7 (Ill.) 1995. Government provided "good cause" for its delay in sealing surveillance tapes which it had made of drug conspirator's telephone conversations, so that tapes did not have to be suppressed based on government's failure to seal them in timely manner, where second surveillance period prevented any need for sealing between periods, government explained its delay between periods as necessary to draft surveillance request affidavit and to get request processed by federal bureaucracy. 18 U.S.C.A. § 2518(8)(a).

> U.S. v. Plescia, 48 F.3d 1452, rehearing and suggestion for rehearing denied, certiorari dismissed Grossi v. U.S., 116 S.Ct. 32, 515 U.S. 1184, 132 L.Ed.2d 914, certiorari denied 116 S.Ct. 114, 516 U.S. 836, 133 L.Ed.2d 66, certiorari denied Demma v. U.S., 116 S.Ct. 114, 516 U.S. 836, 133 L.Ed.2d 66, certiorari denied 116 S.Ct. 114, 516 U.S. 836, 133 L.Ed.2d 66, certiorari denied 116 S.Ct. 329, 516 U.S. 927, 133 L.Ed.2d 230, rehearing denied 116 S.Ct. 556, 516 U.S. 1004, 133 L.Ed.2d 457, certiorari denied Bonavolante v. U.S., 116 S.Ct. 351, 516 U.S. 937, 133 L.Ed.2d 247.

To determine whether surveillance tapes should be suppressed based on government's failure to seal them in timely manner, Court of Appeals had to determine whether government established "good cause" for sealing delays. 18 U.S.C.A. § 2518(8)(a).

> U.S. v. Plescia, 48 F.3d 1452, rehearing and suggestion for rehearing denied, certiorari dismissed Grossi v. U.S., 116 S.Ct. 32, 515 U.S. 1184, 132 L.Ed.2d 914, certiorari denied 116 S.Ct. 114, 516 U.S. 836, 133 L.Ed.2d 66, certiorari denied Demma v. U.S., 116 S.Ct. 114, 516 U.S. 836, 133 L.Ed.2d 66, certiorari denied 116 S.Ct. 114, 516 U.S. 836, 133 L.Ed.2d 66, certiorari denied 116 S.Ct. 329, 516 U.S. 927, 133 L.Ed.2d 230, rehearing denied 116 S.Ct. 556, 516 U.S. 1004, 133 L.Ed.2d 457, certiorari denied Bonavolante v. U.S., 116 S.Ct. 351, 516 U.S. 937, 133 L.Ed.2d 247.

C.A.7 (Ill.) 1994. Tape of conversation between defendant and ex-wife was admissible under Omnibus Crime Control and Safe Streets Act, despite defendant's contention that ex-wife made tape in order to blackmail him, in light of finding that ex-wife's purpose in taping conversation was to turn tape over to government in hope of obtaining better deal for herself. 18 U.S.C.A. § 2510 et seq.

U.S. v. Zarnes, 33 F.3d 1454, rehearing and suggestion for rehearing denied, certiorari denied Bland v. U.S., 115 S.Ct. 2286, 515 U.S. 1126, 132 L.Ed.2d 288.

C.A.7 (Ill.) 1992. As long as recorded conversations are admissible under federal law, they are admissible in federal court, notwithstanding that recordings might not have been admissible in state court. 18 U.S.C.A. § 2511(2)(c).

U.S. v. Goodapple, 958 F.2d 1402, rehearing denied.

C.A.7 (Ill.) 1990. That person who connected pen register did not testify that register was properly connected did not render pen register evidence inadmissible where director of technical operations for Chicago office of Drug Enforcement Agency (DEA) testified that installation procedure was standardized throughout nation and that he had never known DEA to misconnect pen register, and tape printed out by pen register indicated that it was in fact connected to correct phone line.

U.S. v. Beverly, 913 F.2d 337, certiorari denied 111 S.Ct. 766, 498 U.S. 1052, 112 L.Ed.2d 786, certiorari granted Griffin v. U.S., 111 S.Ct. 951, 498 U.S. 1082, 112 L.Ed.2d 1039, affirmed 112 S.Ct. 466, 502 U.S. 46, 116 L.Ed.2d 371, rehearing denied 112 S.Ct. 1253, 502 U.S. 1125, 117 L.Ed.2d 484, dismissal of habeas corpus affirmed 972 F.2d 351, post-conviction relief denied U.S. v. McNulty, 1995 WL 348057, habeas corpus granted in part 1997 WL 666514.

C.A.7 (Ill.) 1988. Intercepted telephone conversations between narcotics conspiracy defendant and codefendant were admissible to show that defendant was familiar with drug trade and that codefendant trusted him; such evidence enhanced probability that defendant's conceivably innocent actions evidenced his knowing participation in conspiracy.

U.S. v. Herrera-Medina, 853 F.2d 564, rehearing denied, post-conviction relief granted U.S. v. Rios, 1988 WL 142226.

C.A.7 (Ill.) 1984. Both Fourth Amendment, by judicial interpretation, and Title III of Omnibus Crime Control and Safe Streets Act, expressly, allow undercover agent to record his conversations with suspect and allow Government to introduce such recordings in evidence.

U.S.C.A. Const. Amend. 4; 18 U.S.C.A. §§ 2510 et seq., 2511(2)(c), 2515.

U.S. v. Eschweiler, 745 F.2d 435, certiorari denied 105 S.Ct. 1188, 469 U.S. 1214, 84 L.Ed.2d 334.

C.A.7 (Ill.) 1984. Fact that government wiretap order was based on authorization to search for evidence of hidden interests in casinos did not preclude use of intercepted conversations in resulting prosecution for conspiracy to bribe United States senator and other crimes; Fourth Amendment did not prevent Government from reviewing lawfully recorded conversations for evidence of charge not alleged in wiretap application. U.S.C.A. Const.Amend. 4; 18 U.S.C.A. §§ 2517(5), 2518(1)(b)(i-iv), (4)(c), (5).

U.S. v. Williams, 737 F.2d 594, certiorari denied 105 S.Ct. 1354, 470 U.S. 1003, 84 L.Ed.2d 377, certiorari denied O'Malley v. United States, 105 S.Ct. 1354, 470 U.S. 1003, 84 L.Ed.2d 377, certiorari denied Lombardo v. United States, 105 S.Ct. 1355, 470 U.S. 1003, 84 L.Ed.2d 377.

C.A.8 (Iowa) 1994. In deciding whether to suppress surreptitiously recorded statements under Fourth Amendment or Wiretap Act, inquiry is whether defendant manifested subjective expectation of privacy and, if so, whether society is prepared to recognize that expectation as reasonable. U.S.C.A. Const.Amend. 4; 18 U.S.C.A. § 2510 et seq.

U.S. v. Clark, 22 F.3d 799, rehearing and suggestion for rehearing denied.

C.A.10 (Kan.) 1990. Under Kansas law, any delay in providing inventory notice to defendant of wiretap did not undermine wiretap authorization or warrant suppression of evidence seized, where inventory notice was provided within 90 days of wiretap order, and defendant failed to show that he was prejudiced by delay. K.S.A. 22–2516(7)(d).

U.S. v. Armendariz, 922 F.2d 602, rehearing denied (#90-3160), certiorari denied Aguirre v. U.S., 112 S.Ct. 87, 502 U.S. 823, 116 L.Ed.2d 59.

C.A.10 (Kan.) 1988. Defendant was not entitled to suppression of intercepted conversations on the basis that order authorized interception of conversations relating to possession and intent to sell methamphetamine while indictments charged conspiracy and attempt to manufacture amphetamine; Government applied to amend authorizing order, and court was specifically informed of conversations involved. K.S.A. 22–2515(6).

U.S. v. Savaiano, 843 F.2d 1280, certiorari denied Crummey v. U.S., 109 S.Ct. 99, 488 U.S. 836, 102 L.Ed.2d 74.

Fact that inventory required by Kansas Electronic Surveillance Act and federal wiretap statute was not served within 90 days after termination of order authorizing interception of communications did not require suppression in the absence of any prejudice to defendants. K.S.A. 22–2516(7)(d); 18 U.S.C.A. § 2518(8)(d).

> U.S. v. Savaiano, 843 F.2d 1280, certiorari denied Crummey v. U.S., 109 S.Ct. 99, 488 U.S. 836, 102 L.Ed.2d 74.

C.A.10 (Kan.) 1971. U.S. v. Cox, 449 F.2d 679, certiorari denied 92 S.Ct. 1783, 406 U.S. 934, 32 L.Ed.2d 136, post-conviction relief denied 1995 WL 351406.

C.A.6 (Ky.) 1995. Failure of government to seal record of intercepted conversation, immediately upon expiration of order authorizing interception, did not require suppression of evidence from recording; government had good faith but mistaken notion that an alternate expiration date, 15 days after first intercepted communication, was applicable. 18 U.S.C.A. § 2518(8)(a).

> U.S. v. Wilkinson, 53 F.3d 757.

C.A.4 (Md.) 1990. Government, which had improperly denied that a conversation between defendant and an alleged participant in a drug network had been recorded as part of illegal electronic surveillance, and had consequently not turned transcript of conversation over to defendant, was precluded from claiming at suppression hearing that independent or attenuated source existed for information contained in search warrant application, as defendant was not afforded opportunity to review transcript of her illegally recorded conversations. 18 U.S.C.A. § 3504(a)(1).

> U.S. v. Apple, 915 F.2d 899, appeal after remand 962 F.2d 335.

C.A.4 (Md.) 1984. Suppression is not a required remedy for technical violations of the law governing wiretap in the absence of bad-faith conduct on the part of the Government.

> U.S. v. Couser, 732 F.2d 1207, certiorari denied 105 S.Ct. 913, 469 U.S. 1161, 83 L.Ed.2d 926.

Fact that application for wiretap order and order itself made no reference to recording of any conversations between user of telephone to be tapped and others who might have been present in immediate area in which telephone was located did not require suppression of recordings of conversations in the absence of bad-faith conduct on the part of the Government.

> U.S. v. Couser, 732 F.2d 1207, certiorari denied 105 S.Ct. 913, 469 U.S. 1161, 83 L.Ed.2d 926.

C.A.4 (Md.) 1975. U. S. v. Bernstein, 509 F.2d 996, vacated 97 S.Ct. 1167, 430 U.S. 902, 51 L.Ed.2d 578, on remand 556 F.2d 244.

C.A.1 (Mass.) 1997. Brief delay in sealing tapes of cellular phone wiretaps did not warrant suppression of subsequent interceptions of oral communications at tavern, where there was no bad faith by the police, no claim of alteration to the tapes, and no other prejudice even suggested. 18 U.S.C.A. § 2518(8)(a).

> U.S. v. Cunningham, 113 F.3d 289, certiorari denied 118 S.Ct. 165, 139 L.Ed.2d 109.

C.A.1 (Mass.) 1995. Failure to comply with provision of federal wiretapping statute requiring local prosecutors to obtain internal authorization from statutorily-designated Justice Department official prior to applying for judicial interception order requires suppression of fruits of unauthorized interception. 18 U.S.C.A. § 2516(1).

> U.S. v. London, 66 F.3d 1227, rehearing and suggestion for rehearing denied, certiorari denied 116 S.Ct. 1542, 517 U.S. 1155, 134 L.Ed.2d 646.

C.A.1 (Mass.) 1993. Defendant seeking to suppress tape recording bears burden of proving by preponderance of evidence either: (1) that primary motivation, or (2) that determinative factor in actor's motivation for intercepting conversation, was to commit a criminal, tortious or other injurious act. 18 U.S.C.(1988 Ed.) § 2511(2)(d).

> U.S. v. Cassiere, 4 F.3d 1006.

C.A.1 (Mass.) 1991. Tape recordings obtained in violation of Massachusetts statute, and testimony derived therefrom, cannot be used as substantive evidence in Massachusetts prosecutions. M.G.L.A. c. 272, § 99.

> U.S. v. Sutherland, 929 F.2d 765, certiorari denied Fini v. U.S., 112 S.Ct. 83, 502 U.S. 822, 116 L.Ed.2d 56.

C.A.1 (Mass.) 1990. Under federal law, federal officers have authority to record conversations with defendant by means of agent wearing "wire" so that, in federal prosecution, wiretap evidence would not be excluded simply as result of possibility that evidence would be inadmissible under Massachusetts law requiring both parties to conversation to consent to use of wire. 18 U.S.C.A. § 2511(2)(c); M.G.L.A. c. 272, § 99.

> U.S. v. Pratt, 913 F.2d 982, certiorari denied 111 S.Ct. 681, 498 U.S. 1028, 112 L.Ed.2d 673.

Evidence obtained in narcotics prosecution by means of agent wearing wire during conversations with defendant was, at most, product of joint federal-state investigation so that suppression of evidence was not required, even though evidence would not have been admissible under Massachusetts law; although initial contact between defendant and law enforcement officers was with state and local police, case was immediately referred to narcotics task force composed of both state officers and federal agents and headed by federal agent. M.G.L.A. c. 272, § 99.

> U.S. v. Pratt, 913 F.2d 982, certiorari denied 111 S.Ct. 681, 498 U.S. 1028, 112 L.Ed.2d 673.

Fact that agent wearing wire on which inculpatory statements of defendant were recorded during narcotics transaction was member of state police department as well as member of joint federal-state task force did not render federal law governing admissibility of wire evidence inapplicable; agent clearly acted in capacity as deputized federal agent for state task force. 18 U.S.C.A. § 2511(2)(c).

> U.S. v. Pratt, 913 F.2d 982, certiorari denied 111 S.Ct. 681, 498 U.S. 1028, 112 L.Ed.2d 673.

C.A.1 (Mass.) 1990. Fact that federal agents failed to reveal previous wiretap applications by state authorities in their application for judicial permission to carry out bugging of premises did not require suppression of electronic surveillance evidence where federal officials were unaware of local authorities' earlier applications and wiretapping despite good-faith inquiry; agents could not be charged with constructive knowledge of prior applications under federal wire tapping statute; even if agents could be assumed careless, despite their thorough inspection of federal files to determine whether there had been prior applications, mere negligence would not have warranted suppression of evidence. 18 U.S.C.A. § 2518(1)(e).

> U.S. v. Zannino, 895 F.2d 1, 106 A.L.R. Fed. 1, certiorari denied 110 S.Ct. 1814, 494 U.S. 1082, 108 L.Ed.2d 944, habeas corpus denied 871 F.Supp. 79.

C.A.1 (Mass.) 1989. Suppression of evidence derived from Canadian wiretap and evidentiary hearing concerning circumstances under which the wiretap was obtained were not required on ground that defendants in United States drug prosecution could not obtain access to sealed application and affidavit in support of wiretap where it was pure speculation that unsealing of packet might have revealed conduct capable of shocking judicial conscience. U.S.C.A. Const.Amend. 4.

> U.S. v. Mitro, 880 F.2d 1480.

C.A.1 (Mass.) 1988. Government was entitled to use conversations intercepted pursuant to wiretap authorization pertaining to RICO violations, as Government's application for electronic surveillance was not subterfuge to obtain conversations related to RICO violations. 18 U.S.C.A. § 2517(5).

> U.S. v. Angiulo, 847 F.2d 956, rehearing denied, certiorari denied Cincotti v. U.S., 109 S.Ct. 138, 488 U.S. 852, 102 L.Ed.2d 110, certiorari denied 109 S.Ct. 314, 488 U.S. 928, 102 L.Ed.2d 332.

C.A.1 (Mass.) 1987. Violation of postinterception tape recording sealing requirement requires that evidence obtained in tape recording be excluded at trial, which is ground for exclusion in addition to grounds contained in general exclusionary statute. 18 U.S.C.A. § 2518(8)(a), (10)(a).

> U.S. v. Mora, 821 F.2d 860.

Evidence obtained through tape recordings of wiretap interceptions were admissible in trial of defendants, though Government delayed in having tapes judicially sealed, as required by statute, where Government presented satisfactory explanation for delay in sealing, as tapes were unsullied, defendants were not prejudiced, prosecution was not advantaged, delay was not intentional, and interval was not outrageous. 18 U.S.C.A. § 2518(8)(a).

> U.S. v. Mora, 821 F.2d 860.

C.A.1 (Mass.) 1987. Even if Congress did intend to permit courts to create exceptions to Omnibus Crime Control and Safe Streets Act paralleling newly developed exceptions to Fourth Amendment exclusionary rule, court nevertheless could not develop exception permitting use of illegally intercepted communications in perjury prosecutions, as congressional authorization of interception and disclosure of communications for purposes of investigating or prosecuting enumerated crimes indicated those crimes deemed serious enough to justify interception and disclosure of private communications, and conspicuously absent from list of offenses were federal crimes of perjury, subordination of perjury, and false declarations before grand jury or court. Omnibus Crime Control and Safe Streets Act of 1968, § 801(d), 18 U.S.C.A. § 2510 note; 18 U.S.C.A. §§ 1503, 1510–1513, 1621–1623, 2511(2)(d), 2515, 2516(2), 2517(3); U.S.C.A. Const.Amend. 4.

> U.S. v. Vest, 813 F.2d 477.

The exception to Omnibus Crime Control and Safe Streets Act exclusionary rule which would allow illegally intercepted communications to be used for impeachment, does not provide support for interpretation of that section as not prohibiting use of unlawfully intercepted communications in perjury prosecutions, in absence of indication of such congressional intent. 18 U.S.C.A. § 2515.

> U.S. v. Vest, 813 F.2d 477.

C.A.1 (Mass.) 1984. Witness who has been granted immunity may refuse to answer questions if source of inquiry is illegal electronic surveillance.

> In re Tse, 748 F.2d 722.

C.A.1 (Mass.) 1974. In re Marcus, 491 F.2d 901, certiorari granted, vacated Marcus v. U.S., 94 S.Ct. 3064, 417 U.S. 942, 41 L.Ed.2d 663.

For cited U.S.C.A. sections and legislative history, see United States Code Annotated

For references to other topics, see Descriptive-Word Index

C.A.6 (Mich.) 1995. Defendant was not entitled to suppression of illegally recorded telephone conversations by his former wife, which disclosed bribe involving defendant, in defendant's prosecution for tax evasion, where government played no part in unlawful interception; any privacy interest which defendant may have had was protected solely by his right to bring civil action against his former wife. 18 U.S.C.A. § 2515.

> U.S. v. Murdock, 63 F.3d 1391, rehearing and suggestion for rehearing denied, certiorari denied 116 S.Ct. 1672, 517 U.S. 1187, 134 L.Ed.2d 776.

C.A.6 (Mich.) 1990. Electronic Communications Privacy Act does not provide independent statutory remedy of suppression for interceptions of electronic communications. 18 U.S.C.A. § 2518(10)(c).

> U.S. v. Meriwether, 917 F.2d 955.

C.A.6 (Mich.) 1986. *United States v. Leon* did not require exclusion of evidence, in prosecution for manufacturing amphetamines, on basis of warrants permitting use of electronic homing transmitters which did not contain time limits but which were obtained at time when there was no clearly established requirement that warrants for such devices limit duration of installation and monitoring. Comprehensive Drug Abuse Prevention and Control Act of 1970, §§ 401(a)(1), 406, 21 U.S.C.A. §§ 841(a)(1), 846; U.S.C.A. Const.Amend. 4.

> U.S. v. Cassity, 807 F.2d 509.

C.A.8 (Minn.) 1988. District court was not required to suppress legally obtained wiretap evidence on the ground that Government improperly disclosed contents of intercepted conversations to secretaries and intelligence analyst. 18 U.S.C.A. §§ 2515, 2517(1, 2).

> U.S. v. O'Connell, 841 F.2d 1408, certiorari denied Patterson v. U.S., 108 S.Ct. 2857, 487 U.S. 1210, 101 L.Ed.2d 893, certiorari denied 109 S.Ct. 799, 488 U.S. 1011, 102 L.Ed.2d 790, denial of post-conviction relief affirmed Cooke v. U.S., 989 F.2d 504, denial of post-conviction relief affirmed 81 F.3d 165.

C.A.8 (Mo.) 1995. District court should not have found that warrant allowing government to use intercepted communications violated *Franks v. Delaware*, which determines whether misrepresentations in supporting affidavit invalidate search warrant, under theory that FBI recklessly failed to investigate material facts in bank fraud case; affidavit was sufficient to establish probable cause that kickback conspiracy was in progress, even if loan transactions, which corroborated insider's allegations

of kickbacks, standing alone were entirely innocent.

> U.S. v. Ozar, 50 F.3d 1440, rehearing and suggestion for rehearing denied, certiorari denied 116 S.Ct. 193, 516 U.S. 871, 133 L.Ed.2d 128.

When considering motion to suppress evidence obtained by lawful electronic surveillance, Court of Appeals evaluates government's minimization efforts on case by case basis. 18 U.S.C.A. § 2518(5).

> U.S. v. Ozar, 50 F.3d 1440, rehearing and suggestion for rehearing denied, certiorari denied 116 S.Ct. 193, 516 U.S. 871, 133 L.Ed.2d 128.

When considering motion to suppress evidence obtained by lawful electronic surveillance, relevant considerations as to whether government is complying with minimization requirements include number of target individuals, ambiguity of intercepted conversations, complexity of acts under investigation, and extent of issuing judge's involvement in surveillance. 18 U.S.C.A. § 2518(5).

> U.S. v. Ozar, 50 F.3d 1440, rehearing and suggestion for rehearing denied, certiorari denied 116 S.Ct. 193, 516 U.S. 871, 133 L.Ed.2d 128.

Total suppression of evidence obtained by electronic surveillance was not warranted under theory that government's inadvertent interception of numerous attorney communications reflected pattern of unnecessary intrusion into attorney-client privilege, where there was no bad-faith attempt to obtain privileged conversations; any privileged conversations should have been suppressed on individual basis at or before trial.

> U.S. v. Ozar, 50 F.3d 1440, rehearing and suggestion for rehearing denied, certiorari denied 116 S.Ct. 193, 516 U.S. 871, 133 L.Ed.2d 128.

C.A.8 (Mo.) 1984. Hotel tape was properly admitted into evidence in drug prosecution even though transmitting device was used without prior approval by the FBI's general counsel.

> U.S. v. Panas, 738 F.2d 278.

C.A.8 (Mo.) 1976. U.S. v. Kirk, 534 F.2d 1262, certiorari denied Green v. U.S., 97 S.Ct. 1174, 430 U.S. 906, 51 L.Ed.2d 581, certiorari denied Hill v. U.S., 97 S.Ct. 1174, 430 U.S. 906, 51 L.Ed.2d 581, certiorari denied 97 S.Ct. 2971, 433 U.S. 907, 53 L.Ed.2d 1091, vacated in part 723 F.2d 1379, certiorari denied 104 S.Ct. 1717, 466 U.S. 930, 80 L.Ed.2d 189.

C.A.9 (Mont.) 1989. Evidence obtained through Canadian electronics surveillance of narcotics defendant would not be suppressed, even if surveillance violated defendant's Fourth Amendment rights, where American agents were not involved in initiating or controlling

For cited U.S.C.A. sections and legislative history, see United States Code Annotated

contested wiretap, and Canadian investigation, which complied with Canadian procedures for obtaining authorization for electronics surveillance, did not "shock the conscience" of the court. U.S.C.A. Const.Amend. 4.

    U.S. v. LaChapelle, 869 F.2d 488.

C.A.8 (Neb.) 1997. Where government's wiretap procedures complied with federal law, evidence obtained thereby was admissible, even if those procedures violated Nebraska law. 18 U.S.C.A. § 2518(5); Neb.Rev.Stat. § 86–705(6).

    U.S. v. Padilla-Pena, 129 F.3d 457.

C.A.8 (Neb.) 1995. Statutory scheme for trap and trace devices does not mandate exclusion of evidence for violations of the statutory requirements. 18 U.S.C.A. §§ 3122, 3123.

    U.S. v. Fregoso, 60 F.3d 1314, rehearing and rehearing denied (#94-3041).

Fact that applicable state and federal statutes did not by their specific terms authorize law enforcement officers to obtain caller identification service did not mean that evidence obtained by this device, which was a lawful trap and trace device, had to be suppressed. 18 U.S.C.A. § 3127(4).

    U.S. v. Fregoso, 60 F.3d 1314, rehearing and rehearing denied (#94-3041).

Federal district court committed no error in declining to suppress evidence obtained in association with pen register.

    U.S. v. Fregoso, 60 F.3d 1314, rehearing and rehearing denied (#94-3041).

C.A.8 (Neb.) 1995. Only statutory remedy for improper disclosure of wiretap evidence before grand jury is suit for civil damages, not suppression. 18 U.S.C.A. § 2515.

    U.S. v. Barnes, 47 F.3d 963.

C.A.8 (Neb.) 1994. In general, admissibility of wiretap evidence in federal criminal prosecutions is a question of federal law, but a wiretap order issued by a state court must comply with state as well as federal law. 18 U.S.C.A. § 2516(2).

    U.S. v. Moore, 41 F.3d 370, rehearing and suggestion for rehearing denied, certiorari denied 115 S.Ct. 1985, 514 U.S. 1121, 131 L.Ed.2d 872.

Although wiretap order was "insufficient on its face," since order was not signed by judge, defect was merely technical, and thus, did not require suppression of resulting wiretap evidence, where wiretap application was authorized by Nebraska Attorney General, where judge made findings required before approving application, where unsigned order, which judge had intended to sign, complied with required 30–day time limit, and where officer believed he was acting under judicial authorization when he directed installation of wiretap. 18 U.S.C.A. §§ 2516(2), 2518(1, 3–5), (10)(a).

    U.S. v. Moore, 41 F.3d 370, rehearing and suggestion for rehearing denied, certiorari denied 115 S.Ct. 1985, 514 U.S. 1121, 131 L.Ed.2d 872.

In determining whether suppression of wiretap evidence is warranted, courts must examine whether violated federal statutory requirement occupies central, or even functional, role in guarding against unwarranted use of wiretapping or electronic surveillance. 18 U.S.C.A. § 2518(10)(a)(i).

    U.S. v. Moore, 41 F.3d 370, rehearing and suggestion for rehearing denied, certiorari denied 115 S.Ct. 1985, 514 U.S. 1121, 131 L.Ed.2d 872.

Leon good faith doctrine required that suppression of wiretap evidence be denied, even though judge did not sign order allowing electronic surveillance, which made order facially deficient, where law enforcement officials watched judge signing parts of the application but could not see which particular pages judge was signing, and where officials left judge's chambers believing that judge had signed order; law enforcement officials acted reasonably and complied with core statutory requirements of federal wiretap law in applying for and executing the wiretap orders. 18 U.S.C.A. §§ 2510–2550.

    U.S. v. Moore, 41 F.3d 370, rehearing and suggestion for rehearing denied, certiorari denied 115 S.Ct. 1985, 514 U.S. 1121, 131 L.Ed.2d 872.

Leon good faith doctrine applies to suppression issues under subsection of federal wiretap statute governing lawfulness of interception of wire or oral communication. 18 U.S.C.A. § 2518(10)(a).

    U.S. v. Moore, 41 F.3d 370, rehearing and suggestion for rehearing denied, certiorari denied 115 S.Ct. 1985, 514 U.S. 1121, 131 L.Ed.2d 872.

C.A.8 (Neb.) 1994. If recordings from electronic surveillance are not sealed immediately upon expiration of order authorizing recording and government cannot provide satisfactory explanation for delay, contents of recordings and all of evidence derived therefrom must be suppressed; to provide satisfactory explanation, government must explain not only why delay in sealing occurred, but also why delay is excusable. 18 U.S.C.A. § 2518(8)(a).

    U.S. v. Maxwell, 25 F.3d 1389, certiorari denied 115 S.Ct. 610, 513 U.S. 1031, 130 L.Ed.2d 519, appeal after remand U.S. v. Lewis, 90 F.3d 302, rehearing and suggestion for rehearing denied, certiorari denied Davis v. U.S., 117 S.Ct. 713, 136 L.Ed.2d 632.

For cited U.S.C.A. sections and legislative history, see United States Code Annotated

In motion to suppress, government adequately explained delay in sealing of wiretap records, where it was issuing judge, rather than government, who specified date for sealing by taking into consideration conflicts in judge's schedule and intervening weekend and holiday. 18 U.S.C.A. § 2518(8)(a).

　　U.S. v. Maxwell, 25 F.3d 1389, certiorari denied 115 S.Ct. 610, 513 U.S. 1031, 130 L.Ed.2d 519, appeal after remand U.S. v. Lewis, 90 F.3d 302, rehearing and suggestion for rehearing denied, certiorari denied Davis v. U.S., 117 S.Ct. 713, 136 L.Ed.2d 632.

C.A.8 (Neb.) 1994. Evidence obtained under wiretap order was properly admitted, even though prior unauthorized interceptions were made by wiretap expert who, with expectation that wiretap would soon be approved by court, conducted audio tests with pen register for brief periods of time on three consecutive days; expert destroyed tests upon completion, decision to seek wiretap order was not prompted by tests, and no information obtained from tests was presented to issuing judge. U.S.C.A. Const. Amend. 4.

　　U.S. v. Lucht, 18 F.3d 541, rehearing denied (93-3271), and rehearing and rehearing denied (92-2569), certiorari denied 115 S.Ct. 363, 513 U.S. 949, 130 L.Ed.2d 316, appeal after remand U.S. v. Kress, 58 F.3d 370.

Fact that affidavit in support of wiretap omitted information that wiretap expert had made unauthorized audio tests prior to issuance of wiretap order did not constitute material omission requiring suppression of wiretap evidence obtained after issuance of order; assuming that such fact was recklessly omitted by police, affidavit and application in support of wiretap contained information from various sources, knowledge of unauthorized testing did not diminish included facts for probable cause purposes, and affidavit, supplemented with information concerning expert's testing, was sufficient to support finding of probable cause. U.S.C.A. Const.Amend. 4.

　　U.S. v. Lucht, 18 F.3d 541, rehearing denied (93-3271), and rehearing and rehearing denied (92-2569), certiorari denied 115 S.Ct. 363, 513 U.S. 949, 130 L.Ed.2d 316, appeal after remand U.S. v. Kress, 58 F.3d 370.

Suppression of all evidence obtained from bugging of drug defendant's home was not required by fact that, even though order did not authorize interceptions of oral communications in bedrooms and bathrooms, tapes included conversations accompanied by sounds of toilet flushing, person urinating, and opening of safe which agents later discovered was located in bathroom; sound of safe opening did not indicate that conversations were taking place in bathroom, and sounds of urination and flushing were brief and unexpected and, once finished, did not provide any clue as to participant's location. U.S.C.A. Const.Amend. 4; 18 U.S.C.A. §§ 2515, 2518(5), (10)(a)(i-iii).

　　U.S. v. Lucht, 18 F.3d 541, rehearing denied (93-3271), and rehearing and rehearing denied (92-2569), certiorari denied 115 S.Ct. 363, 513 U.S. 949, 130 L.Ed.2d 316, appeal after remand U.S. v. Kress, 58 F.3d 370.

C.A.8 (Neb.) 1992. District court properly declined to exclude recording of taped wiretaps despite government's failure to seal the recordings in a timely manner; county attorney reasonably believed that wiretap authorization constituted an extension of the original authorization so that the authorization did not expire until eight days before the tapes were sealed. 18 U.S.C.A. § 2518(8)(a).

　　U.S. v. Sawyers, 963 F.2d 157, rehearing denied, certiorari denied 113 S.Ct. 619, 506 U.S. 1006, 121 L.Ed.2d 552.

C.A.8 (Neb.) 1992. Defendant was not entitled to suppress evidence of pen register, even if county attorney lacked statutory authority to issue subpoena requesting installation of pen register; installation and use of pen register was not "search" under Fourth Amendment, and thus its installation did not violate federal law. Neb.Rev.St. § 86–709.

　　U.S. v. Olderbak, 961 F.2d 756, rehearing denied, certiorari denied 113 S.Ct. 422, 506 U.S. 959, 121 L.Ed.2d 344.

Defendant was not entitled to suppress wiretap evidence, despite contention that wiretap was improperly obtained on basis of false information provided to investigators by confidential informant, where district court could find that officers did not knowingly, intentionally or recklessly include false information on warrant affidavit. U.S.C.A. Const.Amend. 4.

　　U.S. v. Olderbak, 961 F.2d 756, rehearing denied, certiorari denied 113 S.Ct. 422, 506 U.S. 959, 121 L.Ed.2d 344.

C.A.8 (Neb.) 1991. Wiretap or other evidence obtained without violating Constitution or federal law is admissible in federal criminal trial even if evidence is obtained in violation of state law.

　　U.S. v. Brown, 941 F.2d 656.

Even if state law controlled under federal wiretap statute, state law did not require suppression where, at time of wiretap order, state statute permitted judge to order interim reports but did not provide for suppression. 18 U.S.C.A. § 2516(2); Neb.Rev.St. § 86–705(7)(b).

　　U.S. v. Brown, 941 F.2d 656.

C.A.8 (Neb.) 1989. Even if federal statute did prohibit introduction of evidence obtained by state agents where state wiretap order requirements were violated, statute offered no relief to defendant alleging the warrantless use of pen register on telephone line was violation of Nebraska Constitution, absent allegation of violation of Nebraska wiretap statute. 18 U.S.C.A. § 2516(2); Neb. Const. Art. 1, § 7; Neb.Rev.St. § 86–701.

U.S. v. Covos, 872 F.2d 805, rehearing denied, certiorari denied 110 S.Ct. 124, 493 U.S. 840, 107 L.Ed.2d 85.

C.A.9 (Nev.) 1994. Hotel telephone operator did not violate federal wiretapping law, so as to require suppression of evidence leading to recovery of weapons used in murder and identification of defendant as owner, by staying on line after inadvertently hearing occupant of hotel make reference to guns; operator was concerned that there might be a danger to persons in hotel. 18 U.S.C.A. § 2511(1)(a).

Adams v. Sumner, 39 F.3d 933.

C.A.9 (Nev.) 1992. Evidence obtained pursuant to state court wiretap authorization is not subject to suppression in federal court if that evidence was obtained in compliance with federal law.

U.S. v. Homick, 964 F.2d 899.

C.A.3 (N.J.) 1994. Although assistant United States Attorney's own research of wiretap statute could not alone be considered adequate, she acted as reasonably prudent attorney under circumstances when she failed to seal wiretap tapes in timely fashion; Attorney relied not only on her own research but on advice she received from more experienced attorneys, and such advice was consistent attorney's research.

U.S. v. Vastola, 25 F.3d 164, rehearing and rehearing denied, certiorari denied 115 S.Ct. 576, 513 U.S. 1015, 130 L.Ed.2d 491.

C.A.3 (N.J.) 1992. Electronic surveillance tape must be sealed "immediately," which means as soon as administratively practical, or else must be suppressed at trial absent satisfactory explanation from government for failure to comply with statutory sealing requirements. 18 U.S.C.A. § 2518(8)(a).

U.S. v. Carson, 969 F.2d 1480.

Mistakes of law regarding when sealing of electronic surveillance tapes is required will not be grounds for suppression where those mistakes occurred before Supreme Court's *Ojeda Rios* decision outlining requirement that delays be satisfactorily explained. 18 U.S.C.A. §§ 1951, 1961–1968, 1962(d), 2518(8)(a).

U.S. v. Carson, 969 F.2d 1480.

It was question of fact for district court as to what impact, if any, suppression of selected electronic surveillance tapes had on indictment itself or on any other evidence presented at trial by government; district court would consider

what evidence, if any, was procured as "fruit" of tapes suppressed for violation of sealing requirements. 18 U.S.C.A. §§ 1951, 1961–1968, 1962(d), 2518(8)(a).

U.S. v. Carson, 969 F.2d 1480.

C.A.3 (N.J.) 1990. Government's technical violation of custody requirements in unsealing orders when tapes obtained pursuant to wiretap orders were left with private individual for enhancement did not require suppression of tapes; private individual's testimony supplied ample proof that physical integrity of tapes remained pure, and defendant did not challenge Government's explanation that it sent tapes to private individual because it could not have completed enhancements in time for them to be of use to defendants had it relied on its own facilities. 18 U.S.C.A. § 2518(8)(a).

U.S. v. Vastola, 915 F.2d 865, certiorari denied 111 S.Ct. 1073, 498 U.S. 1120, 112 L.Ed.2d 1178, on remand 772 F.Supp. 1472, vacated in part, appeal dismissed in part 989 F.2d 1318, rehearing denied, on remand 830 F.Supp. 250, affirmed 25 F.3d 164, rehearing and rehearing denied, certiorari denied 115 S.Ct. 576, 513 U.S. 1015, 130 L.Ed.2d 491.

United States Supreme Court's *Rios* decision has no bearing on admissibility of wiretap evidence allegedly mishandled by Government subsequent to its unsealing. 18 U.S.C.A. § 2518(8)(a).

U.S. v. Vastola, 915 F.2d 865, certiorari denied 111 S.Ct. 1073, 498 U.S. 1120, 112 L.Ed.2d 1178, on remand 772 F.Supp. 1472, vacated in part, appeal dismissed in part 989 F.2d 1318, rehearing denied, on remand 830 F.Supp. 250, affirmed 25 F.3d 164, rehearing and rehearing denied, certiorari denied 115 S.Ct. 576, 513 U.S. 1015, 130 L.Ed.2d 491.

C.A.3 (N.J.) 1990. Government's delay in sealing tapes obtained through electronic surveillance under Wiretap Act did not require tapes' suppression, absent showing that tapes had been altered. 18 U.S.C.A. § 2518(8)(a).

U.S. v. Vastola, 899 F.2d 211, certiorari granted, vacated 110 S.Ct. 3233, 497 U.S. 1001, 111 L.Ed.2d 744, on remand 915 F.2d 865, certiorari denied 111 S.Ct. 1073, 498 U.S. 1120, 112 L.Ed.2d 1178, on remand 772 F.Supp. 1472, vacated in part, appeal dismissed in part 989 F.2d 1318, rehearing denied, on remand 830 F.Supp. 250, affirmed 25 F.3d 164, rehearing and rehearing denied, certiorari denied 115 S.Ct. 576, 513 U.S. 1015, 130 L.Ed.2d 491.

Government's technical violation of custody requirements in unsealing orders when tapes

For cited U.S.C.A. sections and legislative history, see United States Code Annotated

obtained pursuant to wiretap orders were left with individual for enhancement did not make tapes inadmissible, absent showing that tapes were altered. 18 U.S.C.A. § 2518(8)(a).

> U.S. v. Vastola, 899 F.2d 211, certiorari granted, vacated 110 S.Ct. 3233, 497 U.S. 1001, 111 L.Ed.2d 744, on remand 915 F.2d 865, certiorari denied 111 S.Ct. 1073, 498 U.S. 1120, 112 L.Ed.2d 1178, on remand 772 F.Supp. 1472, vacated in part, appeal dismissed in part 989 F.2d 1318, rehearing denied, on remand 830 F.Supp. 250, affirmed 25 F.3d 164, rehearing and rehearing denied, certiorari denied 115 S.Ct. 576, 513 U.S. 1015, 130 L.Ed.2d 491.

C.A.2 (N.Y.) 1997. Defendants were not entitled to suppression of evidence obtained through wiretaps, even assuming that state's use of pen registers in investigating defendants' operations required warrant under state law and that federal statute requiring state court wiretap authorizations to conform to both state and federal law applied to pen registers; dicta in prior cases requiring conformance with stricter state wiretap procedures had never been applied to bar wiretap evidence, retroactive application of state court decision imposing restrictions on pen register use was not warranted, and state officers relied on several other acceptable sources to show probable cause for wiretap authorizations. U.S.C.A. Const.Amend. 4; 18 U.S.C.A. § 2516(2).

> U.S. v. Miller, 116 F.3d 641.

Suppression of wiretap evidence was not required on ground that affidavits supporting state's wiretap application omitted material information provided by informants cooperating with state, even though wiretaps had been suppressed in state court proceeding, given district court's determination that state officials did not seek to deceive state court or act in suspiciously careless manner in preparing application.

> U.S. v. Miller, 116 F.3d 641.

Defendants were not entitled to suppression of wiretap evidence obtained by state on ground that state omitted one individual's name from wiretap application, knowing that individual was engaged in criminal activity with defendant whose telephone was to be tapped and that individual's conversations would likely be intercepted, even though state court ruled that state was obligated to identify individual when wiretap warrant was obtained; federal law did not require individual's identification on application.

> U.S. v. Miller, 116 F.3d 641.

C.A.2 (N.Y.) 1995. If government presents immunized testimony to decisionmaker other than grand jury, such as judge from whom wiretap authorization is sought, court should invalidate decision and suppress the evidence unless testimony presented was so inconsequential that it could not have influenced government's decision to seek or district court's decision to issue surveillance order. U.S.C.A. Const.Amends. 4, 5.

> U.S. v. Nanni, 59 F.3d 1425, certiorari denied 116 S.Ct. 576, 516 U.S. 1014, 133 L.Ed.2d 499.

C.A.2 (N.Y.) 1994. Wiretap evidence was admissible, even though recordings were not sealed until three days after authorizing order expired, where records were sealed within two business days of expiration, and there was no suggestion of bad faith, deliberate disregard or the statute, or tampering. 18 U.S.C.A. § 2518(8)(a).

> U.S. v. Wong, 40 F.3d 1347, certiorari denied Ngo v. U.S., 115 S.Ct. 1968, 514 U.S. 1113, 131 L.Ed.2d 858, certiorari denied Kwok v. U.S., 115 S.Ct. 1968, 514 U.S. 1113, 131 L.Ed.2d 858, certiorari denied 115 S.Ct. 2568, 515 U.S. 1137, 132 L.Ed.2d 820, certiorari denied 116 S.Ct. 190, 516 U.S. 870, 133 L.Ed.2d 127.

Wiretap evidence was admissible, even though recordings were not sealed upon the arrest of defendants, where a number of individuals who were targets of investigation were not apprehended at the same time, and thus the objective of surveillance had not yet been attained, and where tapes were sealed three business days following arrests. 18 U.S.C.A. § 2518(5), (8)(a).

> U.S. v. Wong, 40 F.3d 1347, certiorari denied Ngo v. U.S., 115 S.Ct. 1968, 514 U.S. 1113, 131 L.Ed.2d 858, certiorari denied Kwok v. U.S., 115 S.Ct. 1968, 514 U.S. 1113, 131 L.Ed.2d 858, certiorari denied 115 S.Ct. 2568, 515 U.S. 1137, 132 L.Ed.2d 820, certiorari denied 116 S.Ct. 190, 516 U.S. 870, 133 L.Ed.2d 127.

C.A.2 (N.Y.) 1993. Suppression of electronic surveillance tapes was not required, even though they had not been sealed until five days after expiration of authorizing order; government claimed mistake had been made in computing number of days involved, and there was no suggestion of bad faith, or deliberate disregard of statute governing sealing. 18 U.S.C.A. § 2518(8)(a).

> U.S. v. Pitera, 5 F.3d 624, certiorari denied 114 S.Ct. 1103, 510 U.S. 1131, 127 L.Ed.2d 415.

C.A.2 (N.Y.) 1991. Even if provision of the Omnibus Crime Control and Safe Streets Act which governed procedures for initial sealing, storage and duplication of oral, wire and electronic surveillance evidence required explanation why delay occurred in resealing tape recordings, such tape recordings were properly admitted against defendant in trial on charge of conspiracy to violate the Racketeer Influenced and Corrupt Organizations Act (RICO) and violations of the Taft-Hartley Act; district court made finding, unchallenged on appeal, that tapes had not been tampered with and were returned in their original condition. Labor Management Relations Act, 1947, § 302(b)(1), 29 U.S.C.A. § 186(b)(1); 18 U.S.C.A. §§ 1961 et seq., 1962(d), 2518(8)(a).

> U.S. v. Vario, 943 F.2d 236, certiorari denied 112 S.Ct. 882, 502 U.S. 1036, 116 L.Ed.2d 786.

Government's applications to amend certain eavesdropping warrants to include conversations not related to offenses cited in original warrant were filed "as soon as practicable" for purposes of statute governing disclosure of information obtained by lawfully authorized electronic surveillance; while Government possessed tapes for four years, it became aware of their relevance to instant case only seven months prior to Government's application to amend. 18 U.S.C.A. § 2517(5).

> U.S. v. Vario, 943 F.2d 236, certiorari denied 112 S.Ct. 882, 502 U.S. 1036, 116 L.Ed.2d 786.

C.A.2 (N.Y.) 1990. Evidence in Racketeer Influenced and Corrupt Organizations Act (RICO) case, consisting of tape recorded conversations of defendant allegedly in furtherance of criminal enterprise, were admissible even though they had not been resealed by court order following their use in another trial; Government satisfied statutory requirement for use of unsealed tapes, that a satisfactory explanation for absence of seal be provided, by explaining that officials had relied upon common understanding that resealing was not required between successive cases. 18 U.S.C.A. § 2518(8)(a).

> U.S. v. Long, 917 F.2d 691.

C.A.2 (N.Y.) 1988. Government's delay in initiating electronic surveillance of home where organized crime activity was believed to be taking place did not provide grounds for suppressing evidence; government affidavit stating that it was impractical, if not physically impossible, for FBI special agents to effect surreptitious entry into the home for the purpose of installing interception devices without significant likelihood of detection adequately explained delay, and probable cause did not become stale during delay and was freshened by visual surveillance of home revealing frequent new visits by alleged criminal associates.

> U.S. v. Gallo, 863 F.2d 185, certiorari denied 109 S.Ct. 1539, 489 U.S. 1083, 103 L.Ed.2d 843.

C.A.2 (N.Y.) 1988. Eight-day delay between termination of wiretap conducted by Delaware state police and sealing of resulting tapes did not render tapes inadmissible in federal drug prosecution; delay in sealing tapes was due to Delaware prosecutor's misunderstanding of requirements for sealing tapes under Delaware law, and there was no showing of bad faith, tampering or prejudice to defendant.

> U.S. v. Kusek, 844 F.2d 942, certiorari denied 109 S.Ct. 157, 488 U.S. 860, 102 L.Ed.2d 128.

C.A.2 (N.Y.) 1985. Even if New York state court decisions required that McKinney's CPL §§ 700.35, 700.40 prohibited order of extension of wiretap from being obtained unless it was applied for prior to termination of earlier order, suppression of conversations intercepted pursuant to state court authorizations for wiretap was not required even though extension order was obtained after expiration of first order, where decisions postdated state court wiretap authorizations, and retroactive application of decisions would not further interests of justice.

> U.S. v. Aiello, 771 F.2d 621.

C.A.2 (N.Y.) 1983. Where United States attorney became aware of recording, of conversation between defendant and informant, only after recording was made, and neither took part in decision to record conversation nor had knowledge that conversation would be recorded, disciplinary rule concerning communication with party known to be represented by attorney did not require suppression of recording though defendant had retained counsel in connection with investigation more than two and one-half years prior to indictment. ABA Code of Prof. Resp., DR7–104(A)(1).

> U.S. v. Jamil, 707 F.2d 638.

C.A.2 (N.Y.) 1981. Introduction into evidence of tape recording of conversations conducted in presence of Government agent did not violate the Fourth Amendment even though agent was not a party to all of conversations recorded. U.S.C.A.Const. Amend. 4.

> U. S. v. Coven, 662 F.2d 162, certiorari denied 102 S.Ct. 1771, 456 U.S. 916, 72 L.Ed.2d 176.

C.A.4 (N.C.) 1983. U.S. v. Hines, 717 F.2d 1481, certiorari denied Jackson v. U.S., 104 S.Ct. 2656, 467 U.S. 1214, 81 L.Ed.2d 363, certiorari denied Bumgardner v. U.S., 104 S.Ct. 2656, 467 U.S. 1214, 81 L.Ed.2d 363, certiorari denied Eleazar v. U.S., 104 S.Ct. 2656, 467 U.S. 1214, 81 L.Ed.2d 363, certiorari denied Peed v. U.S., 104 S.Ct. 2668, 467 U.S. 1219, 81 L.Ed.2d 373.

C.A.6 (Ohio) 1989. Failure to provide defendant with inventory notice within statutory period following wiretap did not require suppression. 18 U.S.C.A. § 2518(8)(d).

> U.S. v. DeJesus, 887 F.2d 114, rehearing denied.

C.A.6 (Ohio) 1975. U. S. v. Donovan, 513 F.2d 337, certiorari granted 96 S.Ct. 1100, 424 U.S. 907, 47 L.Ed.2d 310, reversed 97 S.Ct.

For cited U.S.C.A. sections and legislative history, see United States Code Annotated

658, 429 U.S. 413, 50 L.Ed.2d 652, on remand 552 F.2d 735.

C.A.6 (Ohio) 1957. Massengale v. U. S., 240 F.2d 781, certiorari denied 77 S.Ct. 1296, 354 U.S. 909, 1 L.Ed.2d 1428, adhered to on reconsideration 77 S.Ct. 1400, 354 U.S. 936, 1 L.Ed.2d 1542.

C.A.10 (Okl.) 1994. Wiretap evidence was not required to be suppressed, in drug conspiracy case, on grounds that intercepts had continued past attainment of authorized objective and failed to comply with requirement that they be conducted so as to minimize interception of communications not otherwise subject to interception; conspiracy question was complex, involving numerous players, creating difficulties in determining relevancy of each call. 18 U.S.C.A. § 2518(5).
   U.S. v. Earls, 42 F.3d 1321, certiorari denied 115 S.Ct. 1800, 514 U.S. 1085, 131 L.Ed.2d 727, certiorari denied Bischof v. U.S., 115 S.Ct. 1800, 514 U.S. 1085, 131 L.Ed.2d 727.

C.A.10 (Okl.) 1985. Tapes of conversations involving defendant were admissible when recorded with consent of individual who had agreed to cooperate with Government, although defendant first became known to government agents through authorized wiretap prior to the consent and without obtaining additional authorization for disclosure of earlier wiretaps, since sanction of suppression is limited to cases in which Government has illegally intercepted evidence, and evidence leading to discovery of defendant's name was not illegally intercepted. 18 U.S.C.A. §§ 2515, 2517(5).
   U.S. v. Davis, 780 F.2d 838.

C.A.9 (Or.) 1992. Delay between issuance of search warrant by telephone and certification of transcript of telephone conversation does not require suppression under Oregon law. ORS 133.545(5).
   U.S. v. Nance, 962 F.2d 860, as amended.

C.A.9 (Or.) 1991. Failure of wiretap application to mention prior application listing defendant and another person as targets did not require suppression of intercepted communications where nondisclosure was inadvertent. 18 U.S.C.A. § 2518(1)(e), (10)(a)(i).
   U.S. v. Lujan, 936 F.2d 406.

Suppression of wiretap evidence for noncompliance with wiretap statute is required only for failure to satisfy those statutory requirements that directly and substantially implement congressional intention to limit use of intercept procedures to those situations clearly calling for employment of wiretap. 18 U.S.C.A. § 2518(1)(e), (10)(a)(i).
   U.S. v. Lujan, 936 F.2d 406.

C.A.3 (Pa.) 1997. Federal wiretapping statute did not require suppression when communications were intercepted pursuant to state statutes and were subsequently disclosed in violation of state law. 18 U.S.C.A. §§ 2515, 2518(10)(a).
   U.S. v. Williams, 124 F.3d 411, certiorari denied 118 S.Ct. 698.

C.A.3 (Pa.) 1994. For purposes of determining whether surveillance tapes should be suppressed because they were not sealed immediately after expiration of wiretap authorization, tapes did not have to be sealed until termination of entire wiretap operation so that tapes sealed during running of first or second extension orders were continuation of initial authorization and were sealed in timely fashion. 18 U.S.C.A. § 2518(8)(a).
   U.S. v. Quintero, 38 F.3d 1317, certiorari denied 115 S.Ct. 1263, 513 U.S. 1195, 131 L.Ed.2d 142, certiorari denied Rodriguez v. U.S., 115 S.Ct. 1263, 513 U.S. 1195, 131 L.Ed.2d 142, certiorari denied Gonzalez v. U.S., 115 S.Ct. 1264, 513 U.S. 1195, 131 L.Ed.2d 142.

Admission of wiretap tapes, which should have been suppressed where they were not sealed immediately after authorization expired and government offered no sufficient explanation for delay, was nonconstitutional error so that convictions were subject to evaluation of whether it was highly probable that evidence did not contribute to jury's judgment of conviction. 18 U.S.C.A. § 2518(8)(a).
   U.S. v. Quintero, 38 F.3d 1317, certiorari denied 115 S.Ct. 1263, 513 U.S. 1195, 131 L.Ed.2d 142, certiorari denied Rodriguez v. U.S., 115 S.Ct. 1263, 513 U.S. 1195, 131 L.Ed.2d 142, certiorari denied Gonzalez v. U.S., 115 S.Ct. 1264, 513 U.S. 1195, 131 L.Ed.2d 142.

C.A.3 (Pa.) 1991. The United States cannot use intercepted communication in a criminal prosecution unless party to communication first consents to interception. 18 U.S.C.A. § 2511(1)(d), (2)(c).
   U.S. v. Antoon, 933 F.2d 200, rehearing denied, certiorari denied 112 S.Ct. 300, 502 U.S. 907, 116 L.Ed.2d 243.

Although right at stake in an exclusionary hearing to prevent admission of conversations recorded in violation of federal wiretapping restrictions is statutory, not constitutional, Fourth Amendment precedents determine whether party to communication consented to an interception within meaning of statute. 18 U.S.C.A. § 2511; U.S.C.A. Const.Amend. 4.
   U.S. v. Antoon, 933 F.2d 200, rehearing denied, certiorari denied 112 S.Ct. 300, 502 U.S. 907, 116 L.Ed.2d 243.

C.A.3 (Pa.) 1989. Even if ex parte order authorizing electronic surveillance that was missing one page were considered to have failed to adequately make relevant identifications of agency authorized to intercept communications and of person authorizing that application, such omissions were properly viewed as technical defects not warranting suppression of evidence discovered as result of electronic surveillance; application for order and accompanying affidavit revealed substantial compliance with statute, and accountability had not been undermined, because both agency undertaking surveillance and party authorizing application for surveillance were clearly identified. 18 U.S.C.A. § 2518(4).

U.S. v. Traitz, 871 F.2d 368, rehearing denied, certiorari denied 110 S.Ct. 78, 493 U.S. 821, 107 L.Ed.2d 44.

C.A.1 (Puerto Rico) 1985. Omnibus Crime Control Act was controlling law in federal prosecution in Puerto Rico for aiding and abetting others in possession of cocaine with intent to distribute, and thus, evidence of recorded telephone conversation was admissible, although Puerto Rico Constitution precludes evidence obtained in violation of prohibition against wire tapping. Organic Act of Puerto Rico, § 9, 48 U.S.C.A. § 734; Puerto Rico Const. Art. 2, § 10; 18 U.S.C.A. §§ 2, 2510 et seq.; Comprehensive Drug Abuse Prevention and Control Act of 1970, § 401(a)(1), 21 U.S.C.A. § 841(a)(1).

U.S. v. Quinones, 758 F.2d 40.

C.A.1 (R.I.) 1989. Once authorization for wiretap has been issued, that determination may be reviewed by district court in context of suppression motion, and then again by appellate court.

U.S. v. Ashley, 876 F.2d 1069.

C.A.6 (Tenn.) 1994. Under Omnibus Crime Control Act (OCCA) interception of wire or oral communication in violation of statute precludes use of communication as evidence in any trial or other proceeding. 18 U.S.C.A. § 2515.

U.S. v. Shelton, 30 F.3d 702.

When motion to suppress evidence gained by interception and disclosure of wire or overall communication is made, trial court has discretion to require disclosure of intercepted communications or evidence derived from surveillance. 18 U.S.C.A. §§ 2515, 2518(10)(a).

U.S. v. Shelton, 30 F.3d 702.

Defendant could not establish causal link between alleged surveillance of his telephone calls and introduction of evidence against him at trial, and, thus suppression was not appropriate; defendant did not identify evidence which he believed government intended to use at trial.

U.S. v. Shelton, 30 F.3d 702.

C.A.6 (Tenn.) 1988. After officers were lawfully on premises at which telephone conversations were intercepted, special agent's false

identification of himself to caller did not require suppression of calls as nonconsensual. U.S.C.A. Const.Amend. 4.

U.S. v. Sangineto-Miranda, 859 F.2d 1501, rehearing denied, post-conviction relief denied U.S. v. Betts, 889 F.2d 1088.

C.A.6 (Tenn.) 1987. One defendant, as confederate in gambling business of two defendants who recorded conversations to prevent disagreements with bettors over amounts of their wagers, waived his right of privacy in conversations and thus could not have tapes suppressed that contained those conversations. 18 U.S.C.A. §§ 2511(2)(d), 2515.

U.S. v. Underhill, 813 F.2d 105, certiorari denied Rayburn v. United States, 107 S.Ct. 2484, 482 U.S. 906, 96 L.Ed.2d 376, certiorari denied Tata v. United States, 107 S.Ct. 3268, 483 U.S. 1022, 97 L.Ed.2d 766, certiorari denied Osborne v. U.S., 108 S.Ct. 141, 484 U.S. 846, 98 L.Ed.2d 98, certiorari denied Person v. U.S., 108 S.Ct. 81, 484 U.S. 821, 98 L.Ed.2d 43.

Congress sought to protect parties to conversation from risk that other party will record and divulge contents of conversation by making otherwise legal interceptions unlawful but, in doing so, Congress did not intend to deprive prosecutors of most cogent evidence of wrongdoing because defendants record evidence of their crimes by intercepting communications with their confederates. 18 U.S.C.A. § 2511(2)(d).

U.S. v. Underhill, 813 F.2d 105, certiorari denied Rayburn v. United States, 107 S.Ct. 2484, 482 U.S. 906, 96 L.Ed.2d 376, certiorari denied Tata v. United States, 107 S.Ct. 3268, 483 U.S. 1022, 97 L.Ed.2d 766, certiorari denied Osborne v. U.S., 108 S.Ct. 141, 484 U.S. 846, 98 L.Ed.2d 98, certiorari denied Person v. U.S., 108 S.Ct. 81, 484 U.S. 821, 98 L.Ed.2d 43.

C.A.6 (Tenn.) 1985. Extreme remedy of suppression is authorized under 18 U.S.C.A. § 2515 only when interception of wire or oral communications is unlawful; thus, evidence derived from a lawful wiretap during an investigation of criminal activities and later disclosed to revenue agents who used it for purpose of making civil tax assessments was not subject to suppression.

Resha v. U.S., 767 F.2d 285, certiorari denied 106 S.Ct. 1458, 475 U.S. 1081, 89 L.Ed.2d 716.

C.A.5 (Tex.) 1995. If defendant shows that affidavit offered in support of wiretap authorization contains deliberate falsehood or recklessly disregards the truth, and if defect in affidavit is material, evidence obtained pursuant to faulty affidavit is inadmissible.

U.S. v. Tomblin, 46 F.3d 1369.

Even if investigators recklessly omitted from affidavits to obtain authorization to monitor phone conversations, explanation that some of the targets' admissions were made when the targets were intoxicated and that targets had refused to act unlawfully on several occasions, neither omission supported finding of deliberate falsehood or reckless disregard for truth, as would support suppression of recorded conversations.

U.S. v. Tomblin, 46 F.3d 1369.

C.A.5 (Tex.) 1992. Trial court cannot conclude that interception of conversation does not implicate Fourth Amendment concerns simply because that conversation was carried by cordless telephone, but instead, when faced with motion to suppress intercepted cordless telephone communications, trial court must be prepared to consider reasonableness of privacy expectation in light of all particular circumstances and particular phone at issue; application of Fourth Amendment will depend largely upon specific technology used. U.S.C.A. Const. Amend. 4.

U.S. v. Smith, 978 F.2d 171, certiorari denied 113 S.Ct. 1620, 507 U.S. 999, 123 L.Ed.2d 179.

Defendant seeking to suppress evidence derived from interception of his cordless telephone conversations had failed to carry his burden of showing that Fourth Amendment rights were violated by interception of conversations, although defendant argued that he did not know his conversations over cordless phone would not be private; reasonableness of any expectation of privacy for cordless phone conversation would depend in large part upon specific telephone at issue, but defendant introduced no evidence such as telephone's frequency or range that would tend to show that his subjective expectation of privacy was reasonable. U.S.C.A. Const.Amend. 4.

U.S. v. Smith, 978 F.2d 171, certiorari denied 113 S.Ct. 1620, 507 U.S. 999, 123 L.Ed.2d 179.

C.A.5 (Tex.) 1985. Record supported district court's finding that no evidence was seized, directly or indirectly, as a result of illegal seizure of nonconsensual recording of incriminating conversation between the defendants.

U.S. v. Grubbs, 776 F.2d 1281.

C.A.5 (Tex.) 1984. U.S. v. Butts, 729 F.2d 1514, certiorari denied 105 S.Ct. 181, 469 U.S. 855, 83 L.Ed.2d 115.

C.A.5 (Tex.) 1983. U.S. v. Butts, 710 F.2d 1139, on rehearing 729 F.2d 1514, certiorari denied 105 S.Ct. 181, 469 U.S. 855, 83 L.Ed.2d 115.

C.A.5 (Tex.) 1975. U. S. v. Joseph, 519 F.2d 1068, certiorari denied 96 S.Ct. 1103, 424 U.S. 909, 47 L.Ed.2d 312, certiorari denied Ganem v. U.S., 97 S.Ct. 1173, 430 U.S. 905, 51 L.Ed.2d 581.

C.A.10 (Utah) 1995. Court of Appeals would apply federal law in reviewing admissibility of evidence obtained pursuant to Utah wiretap statute; Utah statute was substantially identical to federal statute governing wiretaps. 18 U.S.C.A. § 2518; U.C.A.1953, 77–23a–10.

U.S. v. Quintana, 70 F.3d 1167.

C.A.10 (Utah) 1995. Government failed to comply with sealing requirement for admission of telephone conversations recorded through wiretap on suspect's phone, where recordings were not made available to state court judge and were never sealed under court's direction; sealing cassette tapes in evidence bag in police department's evidence room did not satisfy sealing requirements of wiretap statute. 18 U.S.C.A. § 2518(8)(a).

U.S. v. Gomez, 67 F.3d 1515, certiorari denied 116 S.Ct. 737, 516 U.S. 1060, 133 L.Ed.2d 687.

Prerequisite to admissibility of telephone recording through wiretap is either that recording was properly placed under seal or government provided satisfactory explanation for its failure to comply with sealing requirement. 18 U.S.C.A. § 2518(8)(a).

U.S. v. Gomez, 67 F.3d 1515, certiorari denied 116 S.Ct. 737, 516 U.S. 1060, 133 L.Ed.2d 687.

Sanction for government's failure to comply with wiretap statute is suppression of recording and evidence derived from it. 18 U.S.C.A. § 2518(8)(a).

U.S. v. Gomez, 67 F.3d 1515, certiorari denied 116 S.Ct. 737, 516 U.S. 1060, 133 L.Ed.2d 687.

C.A.10 (Utah) 1995. Supplemental application and affidavit underlying placement of additional wiretap in investigation of alleged drug activity were insufficient due to their failure to address statutory "necessity requirement," which mandated that wiretap order include statement as to other investigative procedures that have been tried and why such other procedures would be dangerous or unlikely to succeed, or to incorporate information from original wiretap application in support of necessity requirement; thus, suppression of evidence obtained through wiretap was required. 18 U.S.C.A. § 2518(1)(c); U.C.A.1953, 77–23a–10(1)(c).

U.S. v. Mondragon, 52 F.3d 291.

Under Utah's wiretap statute, failure to comply with substantive requirements of wiretap statute necessarily results in suppression of evidence obtained. U.C.A.1953, 77–23a–7.

U.S. v. Mondragon, 52 F.3d 291.

Failure of affidavit and application underlying placement of wiretap to address statutory necessity requirement required suppression of evidence obtained through wiretap, even though wiretap application was supplemental to application for original wiretap which addressed necessity requirement; "common sense" approach to necessity requirement could not remedy failure to include statutorily required information in supplemental application. 18 U.S.C.A. § 2518(1)(c); U.C.A.1953, 77–23a–10(1)(c).

U.S. v. Mondragon, 52 F.3d 291.

C.A.10 (Utah) 1985. Under wire tap statute [18 U.S.C.A. §§ 2510–2520], sanction of suppression is limited only to cases in which government has illegally intercepted evidence.

U.S. v. Cardall, 773 F.2d 1128.

C.A.9 (Wash.) 1995. District court must suppress evidence seized pursuant to wiretap if defendant can show wiretap application contained intentionally or recklessly false information that was material to finding of probable cause. U.S.C.A. Const.Amend. 4.

U.S. v. Meling, 47 F.3d 1546, certiorari denied 116 S.Ct. 130, 516 U.S. 843, 133 L.Ed.2d 79.

C.A.9 (Wash.) 1990. Intercepted telephone conversations between narcotics defendant and third party were admissible upon determination that probable cause existed to believe that drug-related offenses were being committed, that wiretap was necessary, and that interception of nonpertinent calls had been minimized. 18 U.S.C.A. § 2518(5).

U.S. v. Smith, 893 F.2d 1573.

C.A.9 (Wash.) 1988. Codefendant was not entitled to have evidence, which was obtained through wiretap of another defendant's telephone, suppressed because it related to his participation in marijuana transactions, rather than cocaine ring under investigation, and evidence was collected after Drug Enforcement Agency had allegedly accomplished goal of wiretap; wiretap order was formulated to allow agency to intercept communications relating to transactions involving any controlled substance, and goal of discovering scope and details of alleged conspiracy's entire operation was not achieved during wiretap.

U.S. v. Carneiro, 861 F.2d 1171.

C.A.4 (W.Va.) 1990. Failure of state officers to comply with state law governing electronic surveillance when they tape-recorded defendant's conversations by placing body recorder on consenting informant did not warrant suppression of tape recordings in federal prosecution; state law was irrelevant in federal

prosecution where investigating officers, even state officers acting alone, were not acting under authorization of state court.

U.S. v. Glasco, 917 F.2d 797, certiorari denied 111 S.Ct. 1120, 499 U.S. 912, 113 L.Ed.2d 228.

C.A.4 (W.Va.) 1984. U.S. v. Truglio, 731 F.2d 1123, certiorari denied 105 S.Ct. 197, 469 U.S. 862, 83 L.Ed.2d 130.

C.A.7 (Wis.) 1989. Introduction of tape recordings of telephone calls made by federal prison inmate to son who was outside the prison was justified by exception to statute forbidding use of evidence of wiretaps made in violation of statute for wiretapping by investigative or law enforcement officer in ordinary course of his duties; regulations of federal prisons authorized tape recording of all prisoner phone calls except to prisoners' lawyers, and prisoner's calls to his son were recorded in accordance with routine which was the ordinary course for officers who supervised monitoring system. 18 U.S.C.A. §§ 2510(5)(ii), 2515.

U.S. v. Feekes, 879 F.2d 1562, rehearing denied, appeal after remand 929 F.2d 334.

Even if prison investigator who reviewed tapes of telephone conversations between federal prison inmate and son who was outside prison violated Bureau of Prisons regulation by not turning matter over to some federal investigatory agency once it appeared likely that criminal prosecution might be justified, remedy was not exclusion of tape recordings of phone conversations from evidence; making of tape recordings did not violate wiretapping statute. U.S.C.A. Const.Amends. 4, 5; 18 U.S.C.A. § 2515.

U.S. v. Feekes, 879 F.2d 1562, rehearing denied, appeal after remand 929 F.2d 334.

C.A.7 (Wis.) 1989. In federal prosecution for conspiracy to kill a government witness, tape recordings made by state authorities of conversations between government informant and defendants' coconspirator, to which only informant consented, were admissible, notwithstanding that such evidence would have been inadmissible under Wisconsin law in state court since no court order permitting tape recording was obtained. 18 U.S.C.A. § 2511(2)(c).

U.S. v. D'Antoni, 874 F.2d 1214.

E.D.Ark. 1975. U. S. v. Harvey, 394 F.Supp. 228, affirmed 540 F.2d 1345.

C.D.Cal. 1990. Where police acted properly within confines of facially valid warrant authorizing video surveillance, evidence obtained

WEST'S
MINNESOTA
DIGEST 2d

Volume 9

COURT COMMISSIONERS — CRIMINAL LAW ⚷397

ST. PAUL, MINN.
WEST PUBLISHING CO.

were in that other state does not necessarily exclude evidence in Minnesota.
State v. Lucas, 372 N.W.2d 731.

Tape recordings of informant's telephone conversations with defendant and codefendant made in Wisconsin with consent of informant were admissible in trial for first-degree murder and conspiracy to commit first-degree murder, even though tape recordings were made without permission of defendant or codefendant and without search warrant, and thus, would be inadmissible in Wisconsin, where neither Wisconsin police who taped conversations nor Minnesota police who suggested that informant make calls and who participated in the taping violated the laws of either Wisconsin or Minnesota.
State v. Lucas, 372 N.W.2d 731.

It is preferable to use exclusionary-rule analysis rather than traditional conflicts-of-law approach to determine admissibility of evidence obtained in another state.
State v. Lucas, 372 N.W.2d 731.

⚥394.2(3). Cooperation between agents of different governments.

For other cases see the Decennial Digests and WESTLAW.

⚥394.3. —— Wiretapping or other interception.

C.A.8 (Minn.) 1988. District court was not required to suppress legally obtained wiretap evidence on the ground that Government improperly disclosed contents of intercepted conversations to secretaries and intelligence analyst. 18 U.S.C.A. §§ 2515, 2517(1, 2).
U.S. v. O'Connell, 841 F.2d 1408.

C.A.Minn. 1975. Government's alleged failure to correctly identify officer who in fact authorized application for wiretap orders did not require suppression of evidence obtained through wiretapping. 18 U.S.C.A. § 2518(1)(a).
U. S. v. Bohn, 508 F.2d 1145, certiorari denied 95 S.Ct. 1676, 421 U.S. 947, 44 L.Ed.2d 100.

Absent clear showing of prejudice, failure to comply with notice and inventory requirements of statute pertaining to wiretaps does not require suppression of wiretap evidence. 18 U.S.C.A. § 2518(8)(d).
U. S. v. Bohn, 508 F.2d 1145, certiorari denied 95 S.Ct. 1676, 421 U.S. 947, 44 L.Ed.2d 100.

C.A.Minn. 1974. Use of evidence obtained by electronic monitoring of defendant's conversations with a government informant is not

limited to corroboration of testimony of informant. U.S.C.A.Const. Amend. 4.
U. S. v. McMillan, 508 F.2d 101, certiorari denied 95 S.Ct. 1577, 421 U.S. 916, 43 L.Ed.2d 782.

Requirements for laying proper foundation for use of evidence obtained by electronic monitoring of defendant's conversations with a government informant specified. U.S.C.A. Const. Amend. 4.
U. S. v. McMillan, 508 F.2d 101, certiorari denied 95 S.Ct. 1577, 421 U.S. 916, 43 L.Ed.2d 782.

Where government agent testified that he heard voice of informant at all times when he was making recording of telephone conversation, that that part of conversation was accurate and that immediately after telephone calls were completed tape was replayed by agent in informant's presence to verify that conversation had in fact been recorded and that instruments were operating correctly sufficiently established that recordings were true and accurate as basis for foundation for admission in evidence. U.S.C.A.Const. Amend. 4.
U. S. v. McMillan, 508 F.2d 101, certiorari denied 95 S.Ct. 1577, 421 U.S. 916, 43 L.Ed.2d 782.

C.A.Minn. 1972. Where United States delivered to marshal's office formal inventories of wiretap interceptions as required by statute for delivery to defendants and all except certain of the defendants received copies of inventories and defendants who did not receive copies had, through counsel, received copies of application, affidavit and order for interception at or before arraignment and after arraignment counsel for all of such defendants had opportunity to inspect and copy both the actual tapes and transcripts of interceptions, statute was substantially complied with and evidence obtained by virtue of court-authorized wiretap should not have been suppressed with respect to certain defendants for failure to timely serve formal notice of inventories. 18 U.S.C.A. §§ 2518(8)(d), (10)(b), 3731.
U. S. v. Wolk, 466 F.2d 1143.

C.A.Minn. 1972. Affidavit, when considered as a whole provided probable cause for issuance of a wiretap order, even though affidavit contained hearsay upon hearsay; thus trial court erred in issuing order suppressing evidence obtained in wiretap. 18 U.S.C.A. §§ 1955, 1955(b)(1, 2), 2518.
U. S. v. Kleve, 465 F.2d 187.

D.C.Minn. 1973. FCC order which requires that recording devices used in connection with interstate telephone service be equipped with automatic tone warning devices does not apply to conversations being recorded in connection with criminal investigation and

For legislative history of cited statutes

28

For references to other topics, see Descriptive-Word Index

does not require suppression of evidence so obtained or fruits of evidence so obtained. 47 U.S.C.A. § 605.

U. S. v. Buckhanon, 374 F.Supp. 611.

Minn. 1985. Tapes of telephone calls made by witness to coconspirator from a police department in Wisconsin were not inadmissible in Minnesota prosecution on grounds of comity because tapes would have been inadmissible in Wisconsin when obtained without a warrant where tapes were admissible in Minnesota if consent of one party to conversation was obtained and tapes would not have served to deter misconduct by police officers in either state. M.S.A. § 626A.02, subd. 2(d); W.S.A. 968.27–968.33.

State v. Buschkopf, 373 N.W.2d 756.

Minn. 1983. Unintentional failure to name individual whose communications would be intercepted by wiretap does not require suppression of wiretap evidence, at least where application satisfies statutory requirements in all other respects and there is no suggestion that failure to identify individual was for purpose of keeping relevant information from issuing judge. 18 U.S.C.A. § 2518(1)(b)(iv); M.S.A. § 626A.06, subd. 1(b)(iv).

State v. Monsrud, 337 N.W.2d 652.

Every conversation overheard by government by virtue of wiretap is intercepted, regardless of whether or not it is recorded, and thus, procedure employed by agents executing wiretap in listening to but not recording calls determined to be nonpertinent was not acceptable minimization procedure; where intercepted conversations introduced at trial, however, came within ambit of warrant, they were properly admitted, suppression being limited only to those conversations which should not have been seized. M.S.A. §§ 626A.01–626A.23, 626A.06, subd. 4(h).

State v. Monsrud, 337 N.W.2d 652.

Failure to minimize wiretap interception of communications not properly subject to interception under warrant requires only suppression of those conversations which should not have been seized, and not suppression of those conversations which were appropriately seized. M.S.A. §§ 626A.01–626A.23, 626A.06, subd. 4(h).

State v. Monsrud, 337 N.W.2d 652.

Minn. 1982. Witness' consent to have his conversation with defendant taped was freely given, and conversation was properly admitted, notwithstanding witness' reluctance to aid police in investigating his friend. M.S.A. § 626A.02, subd. 2(c, d).

State v. Howard, 324 N.W.2d 216, certiorari denied 103 S.Ct. 818, 459 U.S. 1172, 74 L.Ed.2d 1016.

Minn. 1978. Where one party to telephone conversations, a citizen informer, voluntarily consented to taping of such calls, no warrant was required by either federal or state statutes relating to interception and recording of telephone communications and no Fourth Amendment issue was presented when tape recordings of calls were admitted in evidence in later criminal prosecution. U.S.C.A.Const. Amend. 4; 18 U.S.C.A. § 2511(2)(c, d); M.S.A. § 626A.02, subd. 2(c, d).

State v. Bellfield, 275 N.W.2d 577.

Minn. 1973. Where evidence in prosecution for possession of narcotics was obtained as result of information gathered in wiretap of telephone of one of defendants, and wiretap was authorized by warrants issued on application only by assistant county attorney, and not by county attorney himself or Attorney General, wiretap was illegal and evidence thus obtained was ordered suppressed. M.S.A. §§ 152.01, 152.02, 152.09, 152.15, 388.10, 626A.01 et seq.; 18 U.S.C.A. §§ 2510–2520; 28 U.S.C.A. § 510; U.S.C.A.Const. Amend. 4.

State v. Frink, 206 N.W.2d 664, 296 Minn. 57.

Minn.App. 1985. Tape-recorded conversations of defendant, obtained without his knowledge, were admissible in his trial for coercion, where other party to conversation consented to taping.

State v. Erickson, 362 N.W.2d 398, review denied.

⚷**394.4.** —— **Unlawful search or seizure.**

⚷**394.4(1). In general.**

C.A.Minn. 1979. Records and other documents obtained from defendant during IRS investigation were not obtained in violation of defendant's Fourth and Fifth Amendments rights and were admissible in prosecution for willfully attempting to evade federal income taxes by filing false income tax returns. 26 U.S.C.A. (I.R.C.1954) § 7201; U.S.C.A.Const. Amends. 4, 5.

U. S. v. Vannelli, 595 F.2d 402.

C.A.Minn. 1977. Where police obtained no information in illegal apartment search, which was conducted approximately eight hours after arrest in absence of consent or exigent circumstances mandating warrantless entry, that "led" to search of hallway and discovery by police of green plastic bag, and two searches were linked only by fact that both searches took place in same building and that "fruitful" search immediately succeeded illegal search, evidence found under stairwell was not product of "exploitation" of illegal search of apartment.

U. S. v. Kelly, 551 F.2d 760, certiorari denied 97 S.Ct. 2981, 433 U.S. 912, 53

see Minnesota Statutes Annotated

American Digests Problem

The American Digest System allows you to trace back cases to the earliest times.

In this problem, trace back cases dealing with perjury (nature and elements of offenses in general).

TENTH
DECENNIAL DIGEST
Part 1

AMERICAN DIGEST SYSTEM

1986–1991

*A Complete Digest of All Decisions of the State and
Federal Courts as Reported in the National
Reporter System and the State Reports*

Volume 30

OATH

TO

PHYSICIANS AND SURGEONS

ST. PAUL, MINN.
WEST PUBLISHING CO.

I. OFFENSES AND RESPONSIBILITY THEREFOR.

⚷1. Nature and elements of offenses in general.

Library references

C.J.S. Perjury §§ 2, 3, 5–8, 21.

C.A.7 (Ind.) 1988. Perjury is willful assertion under oath of false, material facts; mere inconsistencies or conflicts in testimony of witness are not enough. 18 U.S.C.A. § 1621.—U.S. v. Peak, 856 F.2d 825, certiorari denied 109 S.Ct. 499, 488 U.S. 969, 102 L.Ed.2d 535.

C.A.5 (Miss.) 1987. To obtain perjury conviction, Government must prove that defendant's statements were material, that they were false, and that, at time they were made, defendant did not believe them to be true.—U.S. v. Nixon, 816 F.2d 1022, rehearing denied 827 F.2d 1019, certiorari denied 108 S.Ct. 749, 484 U.S. 1026, 98 L.Ed.2d 762.

C.A.8 (S.D.) 1987. To establish a perjury case, Government must prove that while under oath, and testifying in a proceeding before a court of the United States, defendant knowingly made a false statement, and that the testimony was material to proof of crime. 18 U.S.C.A. § 1623.—U.S. v. Sablosky, 810 F.2d 167, certiorari denied 108 S.Ct. 109, 484 U.S. 833, 98 L.Ed.2d 68.

E.D.Mich. 1990. In order to convict defendant for making false declarations before grand jury or court, Government must establish that defendant made declaration under oath, that declaration was false, that defendant knowingly made false declaration, and that the false declaration was material to grand jury proceeding. 18 U.S.C.A. §§ 1623, 1623(a).—U.S. v. Ball, 738 F.Supp. 1073.

D.Nev. 1990. Any perjurious activity is subject to being submitted to United States attorney for possible prosecution.—Wiideman v. McKay, 132 F.R.D. 62.

Cal.App. 6 Dist. 1987. Prospective juror who has taken oath that he will "well and truly" answer questions put to him concerning his qualifications as juror can commit perjury by concealing his kinship with defendant. West's Ann.Cal.Penal Code § 118.—People v. Meza, 234 Cal.Rptr. 235, 188 C.A.3d 1631, review denied.

Silence may amount to perjury, considering the mandatory nature of a rule which requires disclosure; disagreeing with *People v. French*, 134 Cal.App. 694, 26 P.2d 310 (2 Dist.).—Id.

Conn.App. 1986. Statute, providing that public defender shall make investigation of financial status of each person who has requested representation based on indigency and cause the person to complete a written statement under oath setting forth assets and sources of income, is descriptive, rather than penal, and its provisions do not constitute separate elements of the crime of making a false statement under oath to qualify for services of a public defender. C.G.S.A. § 51–297(a, b).—State v. Pannone, 516 A.2d 1359, 9 Conn.App. 111, certification denied 519 A.2d 1208, 202 Conn. 804.

Idaho 1991. "Perjury" occurs when witness has intentionally and deliberately misrepresented a state of affairs, knowing those affairs to be false.—State v. Ramos, 808 P.2d 1313, 119 Idaho 568.

Mich.App. 1988. Elements of perjury are administration to defendant of oath authorized by law, by competent authority, issue or cause to which facts sworn to are material, and willful false statements or testimony by defendant regarding such facts.—People v. Forbush, 427 N.W.2d 622, 170 Mich.App. 294, appeal denied.

Minn.App. 1988. Sworn construction statement was not "required or authorized by law to be under oath" within meaning of perjury statute; statute mandating that affidavit of parties with interest affecting title to property had to be duly sworn under oath related only to recordation and admissibility of documents in private action to determine party's interest in property. M.S.A. §§ 507.29, 609.48, subd. 1(2).—State v. Hedstrom, 426 N.W.2d 908.

Tex.App.–Corpus Christi 1986. In order to be guilty of aggravated perjury, person must make false statement with intent to deceive. V.T.C.A., Penal Code § 37.03.—Salazar v. State, 716 S.W.2d 733, review refused.

Tex.App.–Hous. [14 Dist.] 1990. To establish aggravated perjury, State was required to prove that defendant, with intent to deceive and with knowledge of statement's meaning, made false statement under oath in connection with official proceeding, and that false statement was material; statement is material, regardless of admissibility of statement under rules of evidence, if it could have affected course or outcome of official proceeding. V.T.C.A., Penal Code §§ 37.02, 37.03, 37.04(a).—Terrell v. State, 801 S.W.2d 544, review refused.

Vt. 1990. Perjury indictment requires no more than showing of intentional falsity in response to purposeful substantive inquiry; scope of investigation from which perjury charge resulted may include any questioning that could lead to more fruitful investigation of suspected criminal activity.—State v. Wheel, 587 A.2d 933, 155 Vt. 587, post-conviction relief denied 596 A.2d 372.

W.Va. 1985. In order to support a charge of false swearing, person administering the oath or affirmation must be qualified to do so and the sworn testimony, document, or affidavit must be authorized by law to be rendered under an oath or affirmation. Code, 61–5–2.—Farber v. Douglas, 361 S.E.2d 456, 178 W.Va. 491.

Charge of false swearing could not be based on certificate of counsel stating that motion to disqualify judge was made in good faith and with evidence to support the same, since there was no requirement that the certificate be sworn to, even though counsel did gratuitously swear to the certificate. Code, 61–5–2; Trial Court Rule 17.—Id.

Wis.App. 1987. Defendant may be convicted of false swearing for making inconsistent statements under oath at separate proceedings, even though there is not precise identity between questions asked. W.S.A. 946.32(1)(b).—State v. Schlegel, 415 N.W.2d 164, 141 Wis.2d 512, review denied 417 N.W.2d 896, 142 Wis.2d 950.

Judgment debtor could be convicted of false swearing for making inconsistent statements under oath at supplemental and John Doe proceedings, even though questions asked at proceedings may not have been identical, where questions were straightforward questions regarding defendant's ownership of stock, and defendant's answers thereto were unequivocal and diametrically opposed. W.S.A. 946.32(1)(b).—Id.

⚷2. Statutory provisions.

Library references

C.J.S. Perjury §§ 2, 3, 5.

N.J.Super.A.D. 1989. Provision of perjury statute designating materiality as question of law does not ease State's burden of establishing guilt beyond reasonable doubt, merely delegates to court responsibility of determining whether burden has been carried, and is constitutional. N.J.S.A. 2C:28–1, 2C:28–1, subd. b.—State v. Whalen, 563 A.2d 457, 235 N.J.Super. 506.

⚷3. Intent.

Library references

C.J.S. Perjury §§ 17–20.

C.A.2 (Conn.) 1990. Willfulness, in addition to knowledge, was not necessary element of perjury under federal perjury statute. 18 U.S.C.A. § 1623(a).—U.S. v. Fornaro, 894 F.2d 508.

S.D.Fla. 1987. False answer given because of inadvertence, honest mistake, carelessness, neglect, or misunderstanding does not constitute crime of false swearing.—U.S. v. Joseph, 651 F.Supp. 1346.

To prove crime of false swearing, it must be proven that defendant made particular statements in court proceeding, that defendant knew statements to be false when they were made, and that statements were material in court proceeding. 18 U.S.C.A. § 1623.—Id.

⚷4. Proceeding in which oath was administered.

Library references

C.J.S. Perjury §§ 22, 24.

⚷5. —— In general.

Fla.App. 1 Dist. 1989. Capacity in which notary public served in notarizing and witnessing motor vehicle title application was not an "official proceeding," as required to state offense of perjury for falsely swearing to the truth of a statement before a notary for purpose of obtaining certificate of title to motor vehicle. West's F.S.A. §§ 837.011(1), 837.02.—State v. Adkins, 553 So.2d 294.

Tex.App.–Hous. [14 Dist.] 1986. The elements of aggravated perjury are that the statement assigned as perjury must be made during or in connection with an official proceeding and be material. V.T.C.A., Penal Code §§ 37.02–37.04.—Springer v. State, 721 S.W.2d 510, review refused.

W.Va. 1985. Lawfully administered oath or affirmation is essential element of the crime of perjury, and "lawfully administered" oath or affirmation is one authorized by law and taken before or administered by a tribunal, officer or person authorized by law to administer such oaths or affirmations. Code, 61–5–1, 61–5–2.—Farber v. Douglas, 361 S.E.2d 456, 178 W.Va. 491.

⚷6. —— Judicial proceedings.

S.D.Fla. 1987. To prove crime of false swearing, it must be proven that defendant made particular statements in court proceeding, that defendant knew statements to be false when they were made, and that statements were material in court proceeding. 18 U.S.C.A. § 1623.—U.S. v. Joseph, 651 F.Supp. 1346.

Cal.App. 1 Dist. 1987. Juror who gave false answers to clear questions during voir dire, which were not result of oversight or forgetfulness, could be prosecuted for perjury.—People v. Blackwell, 236 Cal.Rptr. 803, 191 C.A.3d 925, review denied.

Ind.App. 1 Dist. 1989. Statements made by defendant under oath at his guilty plea hearing, which allegedly misrepresented his prior criminal record, could serve as basis for subsequent perjury charge. IC 35–35–1–4(d), 35–35–3–4 (1988 Ed.).—State v. Wolff, 545 N.E.2d 39.

In order to utilize defendant's statements made during change of plea hearing or sentencing hearing in subsequent perjury prosecution, State must demonstrate that defendant's statements were: unrelated to offenses previously charged, made under oath, and on the record. IC 35–35–1–4(d), 35–35–3–4 (1988 Ed.).—Id.

NINTH
DECENNIAL DIGEST

Part 2

AMERICAN DIGEST SYSTEM

1981–1986

A Complete Digest of All Decisions of the State and
Federal Courts as Reported in the National
Reporter System and the State Reports

Volume 33

PARLIAMENTARY LAW
TO
PRETRIAL PROCEDURE ⚷500

ST. PAUL, MINN.
WEST PUBLISHING CO.

I. OFFENSES AND RESPONSIBILITY THEREFOR.

⬤➡1. Nature and elements of offenses in general.

Library references

C.J.S. Perjury §§ 2, 3, 5–8, 21.

C.A.Cal. 1982. Because filing of tax return does not require taking oath before competent tribunal, filing of false tax return is not perjury. —U.S. v. Tamura, 694 F.2d 591.

C.A.Ind. 1984. Fact that defendant volunteered the false statement rather than giving it in response to a question did not preclude conviction for making false statement to grand jury. 18 U.S.C.A. § 1623.—U.S. v. McComb, 744 F.2d 555.

Potential interference with grand jury's investigation is all that is required for conviction for making false statement to grand jury. 18 U.S. C.A. § 1623.—Id.

C.A.Ind. 1984. "Perjury" is the willful assertion under oath of false, material fact.—Carey v. Duckworth, 738 F.2d 875.

C.A.Kan. 1984. "Perjury" may be defined as knowingly and willfully giving false testimony relating to a material matter.—U.S. v. Jones, 730 F.2d 593.

C.A.2 (N.Y.) 1985. Defendant, who had right to take stand and testify in his own behalf, did not have the right to lie under oath.—U.S. v. Lizza Industries, Inc., 775 F.2d 492, certiorari denied 106 S.Ct. 1459, 475 U.S. 1082, 89 L.Ed.2d 716.

C.A.10 (Okl.) 1985. Use of defendant's testimony from an absentee ballot fraud prosecution did not violate immunity statute [18 U.S.C.A. § 6002] where defendant's testimony was not compelled by court order, but, rather, defendant entered into an informal agreement with prosecution to provide truthful testimony in exchange for immunity from prosecution.—U.S. v. Girdner, 773 F.2d 257, certiorari denied 106 S.Ct. 1379, 475 U.S. 1066, 89 L.Ed.2d 605.

C.A.7 (Wis.) 1985. In order to prosecute a person for grand jury perjury under 18 U.S.C.A. § 1623, government must establish that defendant's answers dealt with a material fact in grand jury investigation and that answers given were knowingly false.—U.S. v. Serola, 767 F.2d 364.

In a perjury case involving grand jury, government must prove beyond reasonable doubt that questions and answers contained in indictment were material to grand jury investigation, and that at least one of the questions in the particular indictment was answered by defendant knowing the answer to be false.—Id.

D.N.J. 1986. Essential elements of perjury are that the declarant must be under oath, the testimony must have been given in a proceeding before a court of the United States, the declarant must have knowingly made a false statement and the statement must be material to proceeding before the court. 18 U.S.C.A. § 1623((a).—U.S. v. Simone, 627 F.Supp. 1264.

S.D.N.Y. 1986. Attorney, against whom sanctions were sought both as an attorney and as a litigant in a securities action, knowingly testified falsely as to material matters in violation of 18 U.S.C.A. § 1621 by testifying that a letter sent to class members, written by the attorney, accurately reflected feelings of individual whose signature was on letter and that letter included statements that purported facts to which signer had no personal knowledge and conclusions for which signer had no independent basis.—Tedesco v. Mishkin, 629 F.Supp. 1474.

D.C.N.Y. 1982. Crime of perjury in essence is making of material false statement with belief that statement is false. 18 U.S.C.A. § 1621.—

U. S. v. Sherr, 533 F.Supp. 728, affirmed 697 F.2d 300.

Ariz. 1984. Function of perjury statute is to protect administration of government from debilitating effects of false testimony. A.R.S. § 13–2702, subd. A.—Franzi v. Superior Court of Arizona In and For Pima County, 679 P.2d 1043, 139 Ariz. 556.

Ark.App. 1985. If two inconsistent statements are made under oath in judicial proceeding, it is not necessary that it be shown which of the two is false to sustain conviction for perjury. Ark.Stats. § 41–2604.—Fleming v. State, 686 S.W.2d 803.

Cal.App. 1981. Neither statute providing penalty for perjury nor statute providing penalty for preparing false documentary evidence requires actual interference with judicial process as element of offense, and whether either act does result in interference with judicial process is immaterial. West's Ann.Pen.Code, §§ 118, 134. —People v. Laws, 178 Cal.Rptr. 102, 120 C.A.3d 1022.

Ga.App. 1984. Legislative intent of redefinition of false swearing statute was to broaden general definition of false swearing so as to criminalize making of certain false statements, regardless of whether an oath actually was administered by an official; under such broader definition, one who executes a document with knowledge that his mere execution would "purport" to be or would evince his "acknowledgment" that the statements contained therein are being made under lawful oath or affirmation can be held accountable for false swearing. O.C.G.A. § 16–10–71(a).—Holland v. State, 323 S.E.2d 632, 172 Ga.App. 444.

Ill.App. 1 Dist. 1983. To sustain perjury charge, it must be established that defendant made false statement, that statement was material to issue in question, and that defendant did not believe statement to be true. S.H.A. ch. 38, ¶ 32–2.—People v. Columbo, 74 Ill.Dec. 304, 455 N.E.2d 733, 118 Ill.App.3d 882, certiorari denied Columbo v. Illinois, 104 S.Ct. 2394, 467 U.S. 1208, 81 L.Ed.2d 351.

Ky. 1985. When person has made two inconsistent statements under oath, if both of statements, if false, would constitute first-degree perjury, verdict of guilty of first-degree perjury is justified; however, if one of statements, if false, would constitute perjury but the other, if false, would only constitute false swearing, only conviction for false swearing can be justified. KRS 523.040, 523.050, 523.050(2).—Com. v. Thurman, 691 S.W.2d 213.

Defendant could have been convicted of crime higher than false swearing, a misdemeanor, where either of his statements explaining how he had come into possession of diamond ring which he was alleged to have stolen, were false, justifying conviction of first-degree perjury. KRS 523.020, 523.020(1), 523.050(1, 2).—Id.

La.App. 2 Cir. 1982. To support conviction for violation of statute prohibiting false swearing for purpose of violating public health or safety, state is required to prove beyond reasonable doubt following essential elements of crime: that a statement was made by defendant; that statement was false; that defendant knew or had reason to believe statement or material part thereof was false; that statement concerned commission of crime; that statement was made to deprive person of right, privilege or immunity secured by United States Constitution and laws or by state Constitution and laws; that statement was made to an official or agency of state or any parish, city or political subdivision thereof; and statement was made with intent to cause an investigation or any other action to be taken as result thereof. LSA-R.S. 14:126.1.—State v.

Marshall, 424 So.2d 423, writ denied 428 So.2d 475.

Md.App. 1982. "Common law perjury" is giving a false oath in a judicial proceeding in regard to a material matter.—Hourie v. State, 452 A.2d 440, 53 Md.App. 62, affirmed 467 A.2d 1016, 298 Md. 50.

Md.App. 1982. Perjury is committed when the following elements are met: a lawful oath is administered in some judicial proceeding and a person swears wilfully, absolutely and falsely to a matter material to the issue or point in question. Code 1957, Art. 27, § 435.—Smith v. State, 443 A.2d 985, 51 Md.App. 408.

Mich.App. 1981. In order to be guilty of perjury under former statute governing general sales tax or under general perjury statute, false "swearing," that is, statement made under oath, is necessary. M.C.L.A. § 750.423; § 205.74 (Repealed).—People v. Kasparis, 309 N.W.2d 241, 107 Mich.App. 294.

N.H. 1983. A deposition or affidavit which is inadmissible at trial may form the basis of a perjury conviction.—State v. Sands, 467 A.2d 202, 123 N.H. 570.

The offense of "perjury" is committed when a person makes a false material statement under oath in an official proceeding and he does not believe the statement to be true. RSA 641:1.— Id.

N.M.App. 1982. Five elements of perjury are false statement, under oath or affirmation, material to matter involved, in judicial or other official proceeding, knowing statement to be untrue. NMSA 1978, § 30–25–1.—State v. Gallegos, 644 P.2d 545, 98 N.M. 31, certiorari denied 648 P.2d 794, 98 N.M. 336.

N.C. 1984. "Perjury" is a false statement knowingly made in a proceeding in a court of competent jurisdiction or concerning a matter wherein an affiant is required by law to be sworn as to some matter material to the issue or point in question. G.S. § 14–209.—Henry v. Deen, 310 S.E.2d 326, 310 N.C. 75.

N.C.App. 1983. Crime of perjury requires, among other things, that a false statement under oath be knowingly made. G.S. § 20–112.—State v. Baker, 310 S.E.2d 101, 65 N.C.App. 430, certiorari denied 321 S.E.2d 900, 312 N.C. 85.

Ohio App. 1980. As used in statute prohibiting falsification, term "statement" means assertion or declaration of matters of fact. R.C. § 2921.13.—State v. Coyne, 430 N.E.2d 473, 69 Ohio App.2d 63, 23 O.0.3d 68.

Signing of another person's name to notarized document which was accurate in all other respects was not violation of statute prohibiting falsification. R.C. § 2921.13.—Id.

Okl.Cr. 1985. For purposes of a deposition, perjury is committed when the deposition is actually delivered to the court in which it is to be used. 21 O.S.1981, §§ 491, 497.—Graham v. Lanning, 698 P.2d 25.

Okl.Cr. 1983. Omission of testimony lacks an essential element of perjury.—Coleman v. State, 668 P.2d 1126, certiorari denied 104 S.Ct. 986, 464 U.S. 1073, 79 L.Ed.2d 222, stay granted 753 F.2d 832.

Pa.Super. 1982. Absence of retraction is not an element of the offense of perjury. 18 Pa.C. S.A. § 4902(a, d).—Com. v. Lobel, 440 A.2d 602, 294 Pa.Super. 550.

Tex. 1982. "Perjury" is committed by making a deliberate and wilful false statement under oath.—Matter of Davila, 631 S.W.2d 723.

Utah 1984. Mere inconsistencies in the testimony of a witness for the prosecution is not enough to constitute perjury; there must be some palpable contradiction or untruth. U.S.

For references to other topics, see Descriptive-Word Index

NINTH
DECENNIAL DIGEST

Part I

AMERICAN DIGEST SYSTEM

1976–1981

*A Complete Digest of All Decisions of the State and
Federal Courts as Reported in the National
Reporter System and the State Reports*

Volume 26

NEGLIGENCE ⌾121 — PIRACY

ST. PAUL, MINN.
WEST PUBLISHING CO.

I. OFFENSES AND RESPONSIBILITY THEREFOR.

⟜1. Nature and elements of offenses in general.

C.A.Ariz. 1978. In a perjury prosecution, proof that the statements in question were made under oath is one essential element of the crime. 18 U.S.C.A. § 1621.—U. S. v. Arias, 575 F.2d 253, certiorari denied 99 S.Ct. 196, 439 U.S. 868, 58 L.Ed.2d 179.

C.A.Fla. 1978. To constitute perjury, statement must be false, material and made with knowledge of its falsity; a statement literally true constitutes no offense, and similarly, a false answer, if immaterial, is also inoffensive. 18 U.S.C.A. § 1623(a).—U. S. v. Dudley, 581 F.2d 1193.

Defendant's grand jury testimony, to the effect that document shown to her purporting to be a consulting contract had been signed by her on date specified in document, constituted "use" of the document for purposes of statute prohibiting grand jury witness from knowingly making any false material declaration or using any other information, including any document, knowing the same to contain any false material declaration. 18 U.S.C.A. § 1623(a). —Id.

C.A.Ga. 1979. To sustain conviction for making false material declarations to grand jury, prosecution must establish not only that defendant made statements charged to grand jury and that he knew them to be false, but also that they were material to grand jury's investigation. 18 U.S.C.A. § 1623(a).—U. S. v. Cosby, 601 F.2d 754.

C.A.Ind. 1976. Testimony of defendant's wife, who appeared as alibi witness, that her husband was at home on day at issue and that because wife was sick he continued to look in on her during the entire evening and that he checked on her at least every ten minutes was proper subject of indictment charging wife with making false material declarations in her alibi testimony and evidence was sufficient to support conviction where, from the Government's evidence, jury could have found that on evening at issue defendant was in another place for approximately one hour commencing at about 7:30 p. m. 18 U.S.C.A. § 1623.—U. S. v. Williams, 536 F.2d 1202.

C.A.Wis. 1978. Intent to commit perjury does not constitute perjury. 18 U.S.C.A. § 1623.—U. S. v. Laikin, 583 F.2d 968.

D.C.N.Y. 1976. Elements of perjury conviction and conviction for knowingly and wilfully making false statement are similar, but they are not identical in scope. 18 U.S.C.A. §§ 1001, 1621.—U. S. v. Clifford, 426 F.Supp. 696.

Ala.Cr.App. 1978. To constitute perjury, the matter falsely sworn to must be material to the issue in controversy, and the material matter sworn to must be false or it is not the subject of legal perjury. Code of Ala.1975, § 13–5–110.—Murry v. State, 367 So.2d 985, writ denied Ex parte Murry, 367 So.2d 989.

Ariz.App. 1977. Court would reject contention of defendant in perjury prosecution that violation of oath by separate and distinct material false statements can give rise to only one charge of perjury. A.R.S. § 13–561; 18 U.S.C.A. § 1621.—State v. LaBarre, 561 P.2d 764, 114 Ariz. 440.

In order to give rise to multiple counts of perjury, there must be in fact be distinct, separate and material offenses; offense of perjury cannot be compounded by repetition of same question. A.R.S. § 13–561.—Id.

Cal. 1980. Where applicant for aid to families with dependent children has lawfully obtained benefits, but subsequently has material change of circumstances which lowers amount of benefits he should receive, and applicant does not notify appropriate authorities pursuant to eligibility form and continues to receive benefits until next monthly income report arrives, and applicant then terminates receipt of benefits and never completes monthly income report, no criminal liability would result either for perjury or for welfare fraud. West's Ann.Pen.Code, § 118; West's Ann.Welfare & Inst.Code, § 11483.—People v. Jenkins, 620 P.2d 587, 170 Cal.Rptr. 1, 28 C.3d 494.

Cal.App. 1978. Penal Code section defining perjury as involving any false statement made under oath or penalty of perjury is unrelated to section of Welfare and Institutions Code involving obtaining aid by use of a false statement so that conduct proscribed by perjury statute is not dependent upon violation of section of Welfare and Institutions Code. West's Ann.Pen.Code, § 118; West's Ann. Welfare & Inst.Code, § 11483.—People v. Batten, 150 Cal.Rptr. 567, 86 C.A.3d 848.

Colo. 1978. Defendant is not entitled to pervert his right to testify into right to commit perjury.—People v. Cole, 584 P.2d 71, 195 Colo. 483.

Colo. 1977. Charge of perjury in the first degree involves elements of making materially false statement, in an official proceeding, under legally required oath with belief that statement is untrue. C.R.S. '73, 18–8–502. —People v. District Court In and For Third Judicial Dist., 560 P.2d 463, 192 Colo. 480.

D.C.App. 1979. To find defendant guilty of perjury, jury must be convinced, beyond reasonable doubt, that accused testified falsely and that he did not, at the time, believe his testimony to be true.—Boney v. U. S., 396 A.2d 984.

D.C.App. 1978. Elements of perjury are: an oath, before a competent person or tribunal; a statement of false, material facts, and knowledge of the falsity. D.C.C.E. § 22–2501. —Hsu v. U. S., 392 A.2d 972, appeal after remand 439 A.2d 469.

Fla. 1981. In decisional law, "perjury" is defined as the wilful giving of false testimony under lawful oath on a material matter in a judicial proceeding. (Per Boyd, J., with two Judges concurring and one Judge concurring specially.) West's F.S.A. § 837.02.—Adams v. Murphy, 394 So.2d 411.

That a false statement be believed is not an element of the crime of perjury; thus, no criminal result such as a miscarriage of justice need be proved. (Per Boyd, J., with two Judges concurring and one Judge concurring specially.) West's F.S.A. § 837.02.—Id.

Fla.App. 1976. Crime of perjury requires that accused must have made contradictory statements under oath in official proceeding. West's F.S.A. § 837.021.—McCoy v. State, 338 So.2d 52.

Ga. 1977. One can be convicted of perjury only for knowingly and wilfully making a materially false statement under oath and not for a refusal to testify. Code, § 26–2401.—King v. State, 233 S.E.2d 340, 238 Ga. 386.

Ill.App. 1979. To sustain a perjury charge, State must prove that defendant made false statement attributed to him, that statement was material to the issue or point in question and that he did not believe it true. S.H.A. ch. 38, § 32–2.—People v. Cantrell, 34 Ill.Dec. 873, 398 N.E.2d 864, 79 Ill.App.3d 626.

Ill.App. 1978. One must willfully, corruptly and falsely testify to a matter material to the issue or point in question to commit perjury. S.H.A. ch. 38, § 32–2.—People v. Drake, 20 Ill.Dec. 544, 380 N.E.2d 522, 63 Ill.App.3d 633.

Ill.App. 1977. In order to convict defendant of perjury, State is required to prove, among other things, that statement made by defendant was false and that when defendant made statement, he did not believe it to be true. S.H.A. ch. 38, § 4–5.—People v. Dyer, 9 Ill.Dec. 315, 366 N.E.2d 572, 51 Ill.App.3d 731.

Ind.App. 1978. In prosecution for perjury, it was unnecessary, to sustain charge of perjury, to establish that city park and recreation board scrutinized answers to questions given defendant, a public works project bidder, or relied upon false statements in awarding public works contract to defendant, for it was sufficient that defendant made false statement which was reasonably calculated to mislead board in determining who was best bidder. IC 5–16–1–2, 35–1–90–1, 35–3.1–1–4 (1976 Ed.).—Zordani v. State, 371 N.E.2d 396, 175 Ind.App. 297.

Kan.App. 1981. If perjury is committed in trial, litigant is not left helpless; procedure is available to obtain new trial, criminal penalties are available against perjurer and those who engage in conspiracy to commit perjury, and disciplinary rules are available to punish lawyers who engage in such reprehensible conduct. —Hokanson v. Lichtor, 626 P.2d 214, 5 Kan. App.2d 802.

Mass. 1977. To convict of perjury under statute pertaining to perjury by a written statement, the Commonwealth must show that the defendant signed a written statement required by law to be issued and to be verified by a declaration regarding perjury or by oath or affirmation before a magistrate, that defendant in fact issued and so verified the statement and that the statement was willfully false "in a material matter", that is, that it had a tendency to induce action by the addressee. M.G.L.A. c. 268 § 1A.—Com. v. Cerveny, 367 N.E.2d 802, 373 Mass. 345.

It is not necessary for a perjury conviction that it be an object of the perjury to gain a financial advantage; other objects may do. M.G.L.A. c. 268 § 1A.—Id.

Mo.App. 1976. The essence of crime of "perjury" is the wilful false swearing to a substantial definite material fact, and it is incumbent upon state to not only allege but also to prove beyond reasonable doubt that defendant has sworn falsely to a material fact, for the reason that false testimony to an immaterial fact is not perjury. Section 557.-010 RSMo 1969, V.A.M.S.—State v. Roberson, 543 S.W.2d 817.

Nev. 1980. Perjury is an offense against the public only, and subject only to the criminal law.—Eikelberger v. Tolotti, 611 P.2d 1086, 96 Nev. 525.

N.J. 1979. To establish perjury, State must prove that defendant made an affirmation under oath in course of a proceeding, that the statement was false and that defendant knew that his affirmation was false. N.J.S.A. 2A:131–1 (Repealed).—State v. Boratto, 404 A.2d 604, 80 N.J. 506.

N.Y.A.D. 1981. Conviction under perjury statute will lie if a defendant wilfully and knowingly, under oath, makes a statement which he does not believe to be true. 18 U.S.C.A. § 1621.—Matter of Stone, 437 N.Y. S.2d 682, 80 A.D.2d 93.

For references to other topics, see Descriptive-Word Index

EIGHTH
DECENNIAL DIGEST

AMERICAN DIGEST SYSTEM

1966-1976

A Complete Digest of All Decisions of the State and Federal Courts as Reported in the National Reporter System and the State Reports

Volume 34

PAUPERS

TO

PRISONS

ST. PAUL, MINN.
WEST PUBLISHING CO.

I. OFFENSES AND RESPONSIBILITY THEREFOR.

⟹1. Nature and elements of offenses in general.

C.A.D.C. 1973. Where counsel was appearing before district court purely as an advocate presenting oral argument and was not offering testimony, counsel could not have committed perjury.—Stebbins v. Keystone Ins. Co., 481 F.2d 501, 156 U.S.App.D.C. 326.

C.A.Ga. 1976. Essential elements of perjury under federal statute are that declarant must be under oath, the testimony must have been given in proceeding before court of the United States, witness must knowingly make false statement and testimony must have been material to proof of crime. 18 U.S.C.A. § 1623.—U. S. v. Whimpy, 531 F.2d 768.

C.A.Ill. 1974. Fact that grand jury testimony was given by police officer under duress of unconstitutional rule of city police department prohibiting officers from failing to give evidence before grand jury did not require suppression of testimony in perjury prosecution; even in the face of such rule, officer was not privileged to lie before grand jury. 18 U.S.C.A. § 1623.—U. S. v. Nickels, 502 F.2d 1173, certiorari denied 96 S.Ct. 2237, 426 U.S. 911, 48 L.Ed.2d 837.

C.A.Ill. 1973. Government prosecutor has no duty to attempt to get a grand jury witness to recant after giving allegedly perjured testimony; accordingly, the failure to show that such an attempt was made is not an element of the offense of making a false material declaration to the grand jury. 18 U.S.C.A. § 1623(a, c, e).—U. S. v. Gill, 490 F.2d 233, certiorari denied 94 S.Ct. 3171, 417 U.S. 968, 41 L.Ed.2d 1139.

C.A.La. 1976. Perjury is one of the most serious offenses known to law.—U. S. v. Levy, 533 F.2d 969.

C.A.Md. 1973. The essence of crime of perjury is willful untruth, under oath, in material statement. 18 U.S.C.A. § 1621.—U. S. v. Dowdy, 479 F.2d 213, certiorari denied 94 S.Ct. 124, 414 U.S. 823, 38 L.Ed.2d 56, 94 S.Ct. 132, 414 U.S. 866, 38 L.Ed.2d 118, rehearing denied 94 S.Ct. 851, 414 U.S. 1117, 38 L.Ed.2d 744, rehearing denied 94 S.Ct. 851, 414 U.S. 1117, 38 L.Ed.2d 745.

C.A.N.Y. 1971. Not every knowingly false statement under oath is perjurious. 18 U.S.C.A. § 1621.—U. S. v. Freedman, 445 F.2d 1220.

C.A.N.Y. 1971. While a public employee may not be put to Hobbesian choice of self-incrimination or unemployment, he is not privileged to resort to third alternative, i. e., lying. U.S.C.A.Const. Amends. 5, 14.—U. S. ex rel. Annunziato v. Deegan, 440 F.2d 304.

C.A.N.Y. 1970. Essential elements of violation of federal statute relating to perjury are taking of oath, in case where law of United States authorizes oath to be administered, to testify truly, and willfully and contrary to such oath making false statement, as to material fact and which defendant did not believe to be true. 18 U.S.C.A. § 1621.—U. S. v. Stone, 429 F.2d 138.

C.A.N.Y. 1969. Purpose of federal perjury statute is to keep process of justice free from contamination of false testimony; it is for the wrong done to the courts and the administration of justice that punishment is given, not for the effect that any particular testimony might have on the outcome of any given trial. 18 U.S.C.A. § 1621.—U. S. v. Manfredonia, 414 F.2d 760.

C.A.Tex. 1971. "Perjury" is knowingly and willfully giving false testimony relating to a material matter.—U. S. v. Marcello, 436 F.2d 1221, certiorari denied 91 S.Ct. 1231, 401 U.S. 1003, 28 L.Ed.2d 539.

C.A.Tex. 1968. "Perjury" is the willful assertion as to a matter of fact, opinion, belief, or knowledge, made by a witness in judicial proceeding upon oath and such assertion is material to the issue of inquiry and known to such witness to be false.—Luna v. Beto, 395 F.2d 35, certiorari denied 89 S.Ct. 1310, 394 U.S. 966, 22 L.Ed.2d 568.

C.A.Tex. 1966. Internal revenue statute making offense of willful making and subscription of return, statement or document with false statement is a perjury statute. 26 U.S. C.A. (I.R.C.1954) § 7206(1).—Kolaski v. U. S., 362 F.2d 847.

Gist of offense of perjury, under general perjury statute and internal revenue perjury statute, is false statement, wilfully made, of material matter. 26 U.S.C.A. (I.R.C.1954) § 7206(1); 18 U.S.C.A. § 1621.—Id.

D.C.Fla. 1974. Fifth Amendment right to remain silent relates to past events and does not endow witness with a license to commit perjury in answering questions not yet asked. U.S.C.A.Const. Amend. 5.—U. S. v. Prior, 381 F.Supp. 870.

D.C.N.Y. 1971. Defendant charged with perjury in testimony before grand jury was not prejudiced by being charged under the general perjury statute rather than under statute specifically governing false declarations before grand jury, even if special provision of the latter statute whereby timely admission bars prosecution was applicable, since under the former statute government was obliged to prove the true facts while under the latter it would have been sufficient to prove only that defendant's two declarations before the grand jury were inconsistent to the degree that one of them was necessarily false. 18 U.S.C.A. §§ 1621, 1623, 1623(c, d).—U. S. v. Kahn, 340 F.Supp. 485, affirmed 472 F.2d 272, certiorari denied 93 S.Ct. 2270, 411 U.S. 982, 36 L.Ed.2d 958 and Teleprompter Corp. v. U. S., 93 S.Ct. 2270, 411 U.S. 982, 36 L.Ed.2d 958.

D.C.N.Y. 1967. If a prosecution witness is reluctant to testify because of threats or if the witness threatens to lie, he should be put on the stand to determine what attitude he takes; if he then lies he should be impeached and if he persists in lying he should be indicted.—U. S. ex rel. Bruno v. Herold, 271 F.Supp. 491, reversed 408 F.2d 125, certiorari denied 90 S.Ct. 947, 397 U.S. 957, 25 L.Ed.2d 141.

D.C.Okl. 1970. A perjured statement, to be subject to criminal conviction, must be given under oath and before competent tribunal while statement prosecutable under statute prohibiting the wilful and knowing making and using of false statements before an agency of the United States need not be given before a tribunal, need not be given under oath, may involve use of false statement as well as the making of one, and the government is not required to prove that the maker did not believe the statement to be true. 18 U.S.C.A. §§ 1001, 1621.—U. S. v. Stephens, 315 F.Supp. 1008.

Cal.App. 1967. To convict one of crime of perjury it must be proved that defendant took an oath that he would testify, declare, depose or certify truly before a competent tribunal or person that such oath was taken in a case in which an oath may be lawfully administered, and that accused willfully and contrary to such oath stated as true a material fact which he

knew was false. West's Ann.Pen.Code, § 118. —People v. Walker, 55 Cal.Rptr. 726, 247 C.A.2d 554, certiorari denied 88 S.Ct. 60, 389 U.S. 824, 19 L.Ed.2d 77.

Colo. 1966. Under statutes relating to signing of false written statements and taking of oath, to convict defendant of crime of perjury in connection with the signing of a false notarized financial statement to banking commissioner it was necessary to establish signing of a false statement, wilful and corrupt taking of oath or affirming the same and making of oath before an authorized officer in the manner prescribed for the giving of oath. C.R.S. '63, 40–7–2, 98–1–1.—Rogers v. People, 422 P.2d 377, 161 Colo. 317.

Fla.App. 1973. Essential elements of crime of perjury are wilful giving of false testimony on material point in judicial proceeding by person to whom lawful oath has been administered, and motive on part of accused is not required element of crime.—Hirsch v. State, 279 So.2d 866.

Fla.App. 1972. Essential elements of perjury are the willful giving of false testimony under lawful oath on a material matter in a judicial proceeding.—Diamond v. State, 270 So.2d 459.

Ill. 1972. The offense of perjury can be committed only by the use of words; the words used are both the offense and the means by which the offense is committed; thus, perjury differs from burglary, for example, in which the validity of the indictment does not depend on whether the unlawful entry was through the front door, rear door or a window, and from murder, in which the validity of the indictment does not depend on whether the victim was killed by strangulation, stabbing or shooting. S.H.A. ch. 38, § 32–3.—People v. Aud, 288 N.E.2d 453, 52 Ill.2d 368.

Ill.App. 1975. Mere conflicts in testimony of a witness with his prior statements or with other evidence adduced at trial does not ipso facto establish that witness has committed perjury.—People v. Burnett, 341 N.E.2d 86, 35 Ill.App.3d 109.

Ill.App. 1975. To establish perjury, prosecution must establish falsity of statement and materiality of statement to issue in question. S.H.A. ch. 38, § 38–2(a).—People v. Guppy, 333 N.E.2d 576, 30 Ill.App.3d 489.

Ill.App. 1974. Charge of perjury is supported only if false testimony was given under oath administered by authorized person.—People v. Smith, 317 N.E.2d 300, 22 Ill. App.3d 377.

Ill.App. 1968. One cannot be convicted of perjury for having a belief, even though the belief is without factual basis.—People v. Hartfield, 237 N.E.2d 193, 94 Ill.App.2d 421.

Iowa 1972. The essential elements of perjury are (1) a false statement of fact, opinion or belief knowingly made regarding any material matter, (2) under a lawfully authorized oath or affirmation, (3) in any proceeding before any court of justice or officer thereof, or before any tribunal or officer created by law, or in any proceeding in regard to any matter or thing in or respecting which an oath or affirmation is required or authorized by law. I.C.A. § 721.1.—State v. Deets, 195 N.W.2d 118.

Me. 1969. Except as statute defining perjury has enlarged scope of perjury by including therein corrupt and wilful false oaths and affirmations outside the common-law definition of the crime, it is declaratory of the common law and must be construed in harmony therewith and as not making any innovation therein which it does not clearly express. 17

For references to other topics, see Descriptive-Word Index

SEVENTH DECENNIAL DIGEST

AMERICAN DIGEST SYSTEM

1956-1966

A Complete Digest of All Decisions of the State and Federal Courts as Reported in the National Reporter System and the State Reports

Volume 25

PARTIES

TO

PLEADING ⟞ 340

ST. PAUL, MINN.
WEST PUBLISHING CO.

I. OFFENSES AND RESPONSIBILITY THEREFOR.

⟜1. Nature and elements of offenses in general

U.S.Iowa. The essential elements of "perjury" as defined by statutes are an oath authorized by law of United States, taken before a competent tribunal, officer or person, and a false statement wilfully made as to facts material to the hearing. 18 U.S.C.A. § 1621.—U. S. v. Hvass, 78 S.Ct. 501.

C.A.La. To constitute perjury, a false statement must be made with criminal intent, that is, with intent to deceive, and must be wilfully, deliberately knowingly and corruptly false. 18 U.S.C.A. § 1621.—Beckanstin v. U. S., 232 F.2d 1.

C.A.Mass. 1965. The two essential elements to be proven in perjury case are that the statement made by the defendant was in fact false and that it be proven that defendant did not believe statements when made to be true. 18 U.S.C.A. § 1621.—La Placa v. U. S., 354 F.2d 56.

C.A.Mo. Essential elements of crime of perjury are oaths taken before competent tribunal, officer, or person in case in which law of United States authorizes an oath to be administered and a false statement wilfully made as to a material fact. 18 U.S.C.A. § 1621.—Cooper v. U. S., 233 F.2d 821.

C.A.Mo. 1961. Perjury may not be compounded by repetitious asking of same question. 18 U.S.C.A. § 1621.—Masinia v. U. S., 296 F.2d 871.

C.A.Tex. The essential elements of the crime of perjury under federal statute are that a false statement be wilfully made on a material matter in a case in which the law of the United States authorizes an oath to be administered before a competent tribunal. 18 U.S.C.A. § 1621.—Williams v. U. S., 239 F.2d 748.

D.C.Iowa. Essential elements of crime of perjury are an oath authorized by federal law and taken before a competent tribunal, officer, or person and a false statement wilfully made as to facts material to the hearing. 18 U.S.C.A. § 1621.—U. S. v. Hvass, 147 F.Supp. 594.

D.C.N.Y. "Perjury" is committed when a person under oath wilfully or intentionally testifies falsely, and a recantation or retraction is relevant only in showing circumstantially an absence of intent.—U. S. v. Geller, 154 F. Supp. 727.

D.C.N.Y. Perjury and obstruction of justice, or conspiracy to commit either, are crimes. 18 U.S.C.A. §§ 1503, 1621.—U. S. v. Bonanno, 177 F.Supp. 106.

D.C.N.Y. 1966. Essence of "perjury" charge is testimony under oath as to any material fact which witness does not believe to be true.—U. S. v. Rosenberg, 39 F.R.D. 301.

D.C.Pa. "Perjury" is the wilful, knowing and corrupt giving, under oath, of false testimony material to the issue or point of inquiry; and essential element is that defendant must have acted with criminal intent—he must have believed that what he swore to was false and he must have had intent to deceive. 18 U.S.C.A. § 1621.—U. S. v. Laurelli, 187 F.Supp. 30.

D.C.Tex. The essential elements of the crime of perjury are the taking of an oath, in a case where a law of the United States authorizes an oath to be administered, to testify truly, and wilfully and contrary to such oath making a false statement, as to a material fact, and which person did not believe to be true. 18 U.S.C.A. § 1621.—U. S. ex rel. De

La Fuente v. Swing, 146 F.Supp. 648, affirmed 239 F.2d 759.

Ala. Where statement is not under oath, the maker of it does not make himself liable to penalties for perjury if statement be untrue.—Ex parte Williams, 108 So.2d 454.

Cal.App. 1962. Elements necessary to establish perjury are that defendant took an oath that he would testify truly before a competent tribunal, that the oath was taken in a case in which an oath could be lawfully administered, and that defendant wilfully and contrary to such oath stated as true a material matter which he knew to be false. West's Ann.Pen.Code, § 118.—People v. Baranov, 19 Cal.Rptr. 866.

Cal.App. 1963. "Perjury" is false material statement by person who, before giving statement, has taken oath he will testify truly. West's Ann.Pen.Code, § 118.—People v. Gilbert, 31 Cal.Rptr. 920.

Cal.App. 1964. To establish corpus delicti of perjury, it must be shown that defendant took oath he would testify truly before competent tribunal, that such oath was taken in case in which oath may be lawfully administered, and that defendant wilfully and contrary to oath stated as true a material matter which he knew to be false. West's Ann.Pen.Code, § 118.—People v. Davidson, 38 Cal.Rptr. 660.

Colo. The elements of "perjury" by defendant in contempt proceeding are falsity of his testimony, its materiality to issue in contempt matter, administration of oath in proper proceeding, and criminal intent.—Marrs v. People, 312 P.2d 505.

Del. "Perjury" consists of wilfully, absolutely and falsely swearing to a matter material to the issue, and the words "material to the issue" do not mean that testimony for which indictment was laid must be material to main issue, but it is sufficient if it has a substantial bearing upon testimony relating to main issue. 11 Del.C. § 721.—Mumford v. State, 144 A.2d 150.

Fla. The essential elements of the crime of perjury are the wilful giving of false testimony under lawful oath on a material matter in a judicial proceeding, and a grand jury investigation is a judicial proceeding which will support a charge of perjury if the other elements of the crime are present.—Gordon v. State, 104 So.2d 524.

Fla.App. An essential element of crime of perjury is that untrue statement be made under oath with reference to some matter material to main or secondary issue.—State v. Fabian, 97 So.2d 178.

Ky. Statutory offense of false swearing is not the same as common-law perjury.—Greenwell v. Com., 316 S.W.2d 353.

Md. Statute, providing that any person who shall knowingly make any material false statement to procure or assist any other person to procure any license or marriage ceremony in violation of statute is guilty of perjury, applies to unsworn statements as well as statements under oath. Code 1957, art. 62, § 11(b).—Greenwald v. State, 155 A.2d 894.

Alleged fact that penalty of disfranchisement of one who has been convicted under statute providing that any person who shall knowingly make any material false statement to procure, or to assist any other person to procure, any license or marriage ceremony in violation of statute is guilty of perjury may not be constitutionally possible because such offense was not an infamous crime at common law does not remove the offense from the category of criminal conduct, which is subject to punishment under the statute. Const.

art. 1, § 2; Code 1957, art. 62, § 11(b).—Id.

Mo. "Perjury" is wilful false swearing to a substantially definite material fact. Sections 557.010, 557.020 RSMo 1949, V.A.M.S.—State v. Vidauri, 305 S.W.2d 437.

N.J. In general, "perjury" means wilful and corrupt false swearing or affirming, under an oath lawfully administered in the course of a judicial or quasi-judicial proceeding, to some matter material to the issue. N.J.S. 2A:131–1, N.J.S.A.—State v. Sullivan, 130 A. 2d 610.

N.J.Super.A.D. "Perjury" is the wilful assertion as to a matter of fact knowing such to be false with intent of misleading court or jury.—Cermak v. Hertz Corp., 147 A.2d 800, affirmed 147 A.2d 795.

N.M. Wilfully testifying falsely is the gravamen of perjury; offense involves more than giving of false testimony knowingly. 1953 Comp. § 40–32–2.—State v. Reed, 306 P.2d 640.

A.D. Perjury is not committed by failing to make statement of facts, no matter how relevant or material such statement, if made, might be to subject matter in hand, and no matter how mandatory rule might be requiring such statement to be made as prerequisite to accomplishment of purpose of affidavit.—People v. Dodge, 212 N.Y.S.2d 526.

Sup. 1963. Essential element of the crime of perjury consists of the making of a false statement under oath.—People v. Levitas, 243 N.Y.S.2d 234.

Co.Ct. Charge of perjury must be based upon the wilful and knowing giving of false testimony under oath.—People v. Romler, 215 N.Y.S.2d 315.

Co.Ct. 1964. Essential element of perjury is the making of a false statement under oath. Penal Law, §§ 1620, 1620–a.—People v. Gould, 246 N.Y.S.2d 758.

N.C. "Perjury" consists of false statement under oath, knowingly, wilfully and designedly made, in proceeding in court of competent jurisdiction, or concerning matter wherein affiant is required by law to be sworn, as to some matter material to issue or point in question. G.S. § 14–209.—State v. Lucas, 92 S.E. 2d 401.

N.C. Perjury and subornation of perjury are criminal offenses. G.S. §§ 14–209, 14–210.—Brewer v. Carolina Coach Co., 116 S. E.2d 725.

Pa.Super. The crime of "perjury" has a number of elements such as an oath to tell the truth must be taken by the accused to be administered by legal authority in a judicial proceeding or statutory affidavit; accused must have testified in such proceeding; his testimony must be material; testimony assigned as perjury must be false and must be given wilfully and corruptly and with knowledge of its falsity or given recklessly and for the purpose of having it believed.—Com. v. Leitch, 137 A.2d 909.

S.C. 1966. Perjury or false swearing is a species of intrinsic, not extrinsic, fraud.—Corley v. Centennial Const. Co., 146 S.E.2d 609.

W.Va. At common law, "perjury" was a misdemeanor, defined as wilfully giving under oath, in judicial proceeding or course of justice, false testimony material to issue or point of inquiry.—State v. Crowder, 123 S.E.2d 42.

Facts necessary to constitute perjury always include false swearing, but separate statutory offense of false swearing in many instances does not include perjury. Code, 61–5–1, 61–5–2.—Id.

For subsequent case history Information, see Table of Cases

SIXTH
DECENNIAL DIGEST

AMERICAN DIGEST SYSTEM

1946-1956

*A Complete Digest of All Decisions of the State and
Federal Courts as Reported in the National
Reporter System and the State Reports*

Volume 25

PAUPERS—QUO WARRANTO

ST. PAUL, MINN.
WEST PUBLISHING CO.

II. PROSECUTION AND PUNISHMENT—Continued.

For references to other topics, see Descriptive-Word Index.

I. OFFENSES AND RESPONSIBILITY THEREFOR

🔑1. Nature and elements of offenses in general

App.D.C. Perjury is committed when one states, contrary to his oath, any material matter which he does not believe to be true. D.C.Code 1940, § 22–2501.—Pyle v. U. S., 156 F.2d 852, 81 U.S.App.D.C. 209.

App.D.C. The making of false statement of lien under oath in application for certificate or duplicate certificate of title for motor vehicle in the District of Columbia must be prosecuted by corporation counsel in the name of the District of Columbia, under the Motor Vehicle Lien Law, rather than by the United States attorney in the name of the United States under the general perjury statute. D.C.Code 1940, §§ 22–2501, 40–701 to 715, 40–702, 40–714.—Shelton v. U. S., 165 F.2d 241, 83 U.S.App.D.C. 32.

C.A.Ala. Essential elements of federal crime of perjury are oath authorized by federal law and taken before competent tribunal, officer, or person and false statement willfully made as to facts material to the hearing. 18 U.S.C.A. § 1621.—Harrell v. U. S., 220 F.2d 516.

C.A.N.Y. False statements under oath before one who has no legal authority to administer oath of public

nature, or before one who is authorized to administer some kind of oaths, but not one which is brought in question, cannot amount to perjury at common law, or subject party making it to prosecution for statutory offense of willfully false swearing, and to constitute such offense oath must be permitted or required, by at least laws of United States, and be administered by some tribunal, officer, or person authorized by such laws to administer oaths in respect of particular matters to which it relates. Nationality Act of 1940, § 346(a) (1), 8 U.S.C.A. § 746(a) (1).—U. S. v. Obermeier, 186 F.2d 243, certiorari denied Obermeier v. U. S., 71 S.Ct. 569, 340 U.S. 951, 95 L.Ed. 685, certiorari denied U. S. v. Obermeier, 71 S.Ct. 573, 340 U.S. 951, 95 L.Ed. 685.

C.A.N.Y. "Perjury" consists in testifying to the truth of a fact which the accused does not believe to be true. 18 U.S.C.A. § 1621.—U. S. v. Remington, 191 F.2d 246, certiarori denied 72 S.Ct. 580, 343 U.S. 907, 96 L.Ed. ——.

C.A.Pa. "Perjury" among other things is false swearing in a material matter requiring affidavit or oath to be taken, with knowledge on part of defendant that false swearing is false. 18 U.S.C.A. § 1621.—U. S. v. Seavey, 180 F.2d 837, certiorari denied 70 S.Ct. 1023, 339 U.S. 979, 94 L.Ed. ——.

C.A.Pa. "Perjury" is the willful knowing and corrupt giving under oath

of false testimony material to the issue or point of inquiry, and criminal intent is an essential element. 18 U.S.C.A. § 1621.—U. S. v. Rose, 215 F.2d 617.

D.C.D.C. Gist of perjury offense is false oath before a competent tribunal. D.C.Code 1951, §§ 22–2501, 23–204; 18 U.S.C.A. §§ 1621, 3771.—U. S. v. Young, 113 F.Supp. 20, affirmed 212 F.2d 236, certiorari denied 74 S.Ct. 870, 347 U.S. 1015, 98 L.Ed. 1137.

D.C.D.C. The essential facts constituting "perjury" are that defendant appeared before a competent tribunal, was duly sworn, and willfully gave specified testimony, material to the inquiry being pursued by tribunal, which, to defendant's knowledge, was false.—U. S. v. Young, 14 F.R.D. 406.

D.C.Mich. "Perjury" means the willful giving of false testimony as to any material matter before competent tribunal, under oath.—U. S. v. Allen, 131 F.Supp. 323.

D.C.Okl. Perjury as such does not give rise to civil liability, but is solely punishable by criminal action against perjurer.—Graham v. Morgan, 129 F.Supp. 199, cause remanded 228 F.2d 625.

Ariz. Under statute providing that every person who is required to make any return, statement or report under oath, and who wilfully makes and delivers any return, statement or report,

FIFTH
DECENNIAL DIGEST

AMERICAN DIGE$T SYSTEM

1936 - 1946

Volume 36

Patents ⟜ 97 — Pleading ⟜ 228

A Complete Digest Of All Decisions

Of The

State And Federal Courts As Reported In

The National Reporter System

And The State Reports

By the Publisher's Editorial Staff

ST. PAUL, MINN.

WEST PUBLISHING CO.

I. OFFENSES AND RESPONSIBILITY THEREFOR.

⚖1. Nature and elements of offenses in general.

U.S.Neb. 1937. Deliberate material falsification under oath constitutes crime of "perjury," and crime is complete when a witness' statement has once been made. 18 U.S.C.A. § 1622.—U. S. v. Norris, 57 S.Ct. 535, 300 U.S. 564, 81 L.Ed. 808.

Oath administered to witness calls on him freely to disclose the truth in the first instance and not to put court and parties to disadvantage, hindrance, and delay of ultimately extracting the truth by cross-examination, by extraneous investigation, or other collateral means.—U. S. v. Norris, 57 S. Ct. 535, 300 U.S. 564, 81 L.Ed. 808.

C.C.A.Mo. 1943. Deliberate material falsification under oath constitutes crime of "perjury". 18 U.S.C.A. § 1622.—Fotie v. U. S., 137 F.2d 831.

C.C.A.N.Y. 1941. A witness may be guilty of contempt of court by obstructing justice and also be guilty of perjury. 28 U.S.C.A. § 459.—In re Gottman, 118 F.2d 425.

C.C.A.Pa. 1939. "Perjury" and its "subornation" are considered as part and parcel of the same offense, since no distinction between procurement and perpetration obtains. 18 U.S.C.A. §§ 2, 1621, 1622.—U. S. v. Silverman, 106 F.2d 750.

D.C.N.Y. 1941. Perjury which obstructs administration of justice may be punished by indictment as well as by contempt, and one remedy does not preclude the other. 28 U.S.C.A. § 459.—U. S. v. Johansen, 36 F.Supp. 30.

Ala. 1941. The offense of perjury is committed, if at all, as soon as the false evidence is given, and if it was then material, the question of materiality is settled in so far as it affects a subsequent charge of perjury, regardless of the result reached on that trial.—Wright v. State, 3 So.2d 326, 241 Ala. 529.

Cal.App. 1943. A false statement need not be made for the purpose of injuring another in order to constitute "perjury". Pen. Code, § 118.—People v. Darcy, 139 P.2d 118, 59 Cal.App.2d 342.

One who, being required by law to make a statement under oath, willfully and knowingly falsifies such statement, purportedly made under oath, in any particular, is guilty of "perjury" as a matter of law, regardless of whether oath was in fact taken or whether maker knew the materiality of the falsehood, the offense being completed upon delivery of affidavit to another person, with intent that it be uttered or published as true. Pen.Code, §§ 118, 121, 123, 124, 129.—People v. Darcy, 139 P.2d 118, 59 Cal.App.2d 342.

Fla. 1943. In order to sustain a conviction for perjury, not only must the substance of alleged false testimony be proven but it must be also proven that such testimony was material to issue upon which trial was had and was in fact false testimony and that accused knew of its falsity and wilfully swore to it as true.—Keir v. State, 11 So.2d 886, 152 Fla. 389.

Ga.App. 1942. The essential elements of "false swearing" consist in willfully, knowingly, absolutely and falsely swearing under oath or affirmation on a matter concerning which a party could legally be sworn and on oath administered by one legally authorized to administer it. Code, § 26-4003.—Smith v. State, 19 S.E.2d 168, 66 Ga.App. 669.

Ga.App. 1942. "Perjury" is willful assertion as to matter of fact, opinion, belief, or knowledge by a witness in judicial proceeding as part of his evidence, either on oath or in any substituted form allowed by law, whether in open court or in affidavit or otherwise, with knowledge of falsity thereof and intent to mislead court, jury, or person holding proceeding and consists in swearing falsely and corruptly without probable cause for belief, not in swearing rashly or inconsiderately according to belief.—Hicks v. State, 21 S.E.2d 113, 67 Ga.App. 475.

Idaho 1939. The law does not undertake to punish every false statement made in litigation or otherwise, but only willful falsehoods about a material matter at issue or involved in some matter requiring the sanction of an oath. Code 1932, § 19-1326.—State v. Lowe, 88 P.2d 502, 60 Idaho 98.

Ill. 1944. "Perjury" is willfully, corruptly, and falsely testifying in a matter material to the issue or point in question.—In re Obartuch, 54 N.E.2d 470, 386 Ill. 323.

Ky. 1943. To constitute offense of "false swearing", it must appear that matter sworn to was judicially pending or was being investigated by grand jury, or was a subject on which accused could legally have been sworn, or on which he was required to be sworn. KRS 432.170.—Capps v. Com., 172 S.W.2d 610, 294 Ky. 743.

To constitute "false swearing", the oath need not, as in "perjury", be taken in a matter judicially pending or any matter material to any point in question, but it is only necessary that the false statement should have been willfully made with the knowledge of its falsity on a subject in reference to which accused might have been legally sworn and that the oath was administered by an officer authorized to administer it. KRS 432.170.—Capps v. Com., 172 S.W.2d 610, 294 Ky. 743.

La. 1941. It is a criminal offense for a police officer to strike and mistreat a prisoner, and if a confession is obtained by that means and officers testify falsely they are subject to charges of "perjury," and a state-

FOURTH DECENNIAL DIGEST

AMERICAN DIGEST SYSTEM

A COMPLETE DIGEST OF ALL DECISIONS
OF THE
STATE AND FEDERAL COURTS AS REPORTED IN
THE NATIONAL REPORTER SYSTEM
AND THE STATE REPORTS

1926 TO 1936

Volume 25
Patents—Pleading

BY THE PUBLISHER'S EDITORIAL STAFF

ST. PAUL, MINN.
WEST PUBLISHING CO.

II. PROSECUTION AND PUNISHMENT—Continued.

For references to other topics, see Descriptive-Word Index.

I. OFFENSES AND RESPONSIBILITY THEREFOR.

☞1. Nature and elements of offenses in general.

C.C.A.N.Y. 1926. Crime of perjury in affidavit is complete, when oath is taken with necessary intent, and it is immaterial and irrelevant that false affidavit is never used.—Steinberg v. U. S., 14 F.2d 564.

C.C.A.N.Y. 1932. Crime of perjury is complete moment oath is taken.—U. S. ex rel. Starr v. Mulligan, 59 F.2d 200.

C.C.A.Pa. 1935. Word "perjury" as used in federal perjury statute means the willful giving of false testimony as to any material matter before a competent tribunal under oath. Cr.Code § 125, 18 U.S.C.A. § 231.—U. S. v. Slutzky, 79 F.2d 504.

Ala. 1935. Where license tax statute required seller of goods advertising sale as bankrupt, trustee, or fire sale, etc., to make affidavit, oath thereunder, if willfully, corruptly, and falsely made, constitutes perjury under statute. Gen.Acts 1919, p. 395, § 361, schedule 51; Code 1923, § 5167.—State v. Kartus, 162 So. 533, 230 Ala. 352, 101 A.L.R. 1336, answers conformed to 162 So. 538, 26 Ala.App. 446, certiorari denied 162 So. 541, 230 Ala. 357.

Cal.App. 1927. Not every false swearing constitutes perjury, even though it be as to material facts.—People v. Millsap, 260 P. 378, 85 Cal.App. 732.

Cal.App. 1933. Perjury is not committed by failure to state fact in affidavit. Pen.Code, §§ 118, 118a.—People v. French, 26 P.2d 310, 134 Cal.App. 694.

Ky. 1935. To constitute offense of "false swearing" it must appear that matter sworn to was judicially pending, or was being investigated by grand jury, was a subject on which defendant could legally have been sworn, or on which he was required to be sworn. Ky.St. § 1174.—Commonwealth v. Strunk, 83 S.W.2d 861, 260 Ky. 35.

Mont. 1926. Generally, perjury will be predicated only on a false statement of a material fact made under oath, in view of Rev. Codes 1921, § 10878.—State v. District Court of Twentieth Judicial Dist. in and for Roosevelt County, 244 P. 280, 75 Mont. 476.

Mont. 1928. Testimony stating as true that which witness has no reason to believe true is equivalent to stating that which he knows is false. Rev.Codes 1921, § 10878.—In re McCue, 261 P. 341, 80 Mont. 537.

Mont. 1930. "Perjury" consists in willfully, intentionally, and corruptly falsifying under oath. Rev.Codes 1921, §§ 10878, 10887.—State v. Jackson, 293 P. 309, 88 Mont. 420.

N.Y.Sup. 1933. To establish perjury, people must prove false swearing, with corrupt or willful intent, as to matter material to issue in trial.—People v. Kresel, 264 N.Y.S. 464, 147 Misc. 241.

N.C. 1931. Requisites of "perjury" are false oath, lawfully administered in judicial proceeding or in course of justice, and willfully and corruptly taken respecting material matter. C. S. § 4364.—State v. Dowd, 161 S.E. 205, 201 N.C. 714.

At common law, false swearing and perjury are distinct offenses.—State v. Dowd, 161 S.E. 205, 201 N.C. 714.

N.D. 1926. Crime of "perjury" is committed when evidence given by accused is material, false and willful.—State v. Singleton, 207 N.W. 226, 53 N.D. 573.

1926

THIRD
DECENNIAL EDITION

OF THE

AMERICAN DIGEST

A COMPLETE DIGEST OF ALL
REPORTED CASES FROM 1916 TO 1926

VOLUME 22

PAUPERS—PROSTITUTION

ST. PAUL
WEST PUBLISHING CO.
1929

II. Prosecution and Punishment—Continued.

For related matters under other topics, see Descriptive-Word Indexes.

I. OFFENSES AND RESPONSIBILITY THEREFOR.

☞1. **Nature and elements of offenses in general.**

Amendment of statute on which proceeding was based, see Criminal Law, ☞14.

(U.S.D.C.Ariz.1922) Since the adoption of the Seventeenth Amendment, providing for election of Senators by popular vote, a candidate at such election is not a "candidate for nomination at any primary election or nominating convention or for indorsement at any general or special election or election by the

Legislature of any state," and is not required by the terms of Corrupt Practices Act, § 8 (Comp. St. § 195), to file a statement of receipts and expenditures, and an indictment for perjury cannot be predicated on a false oath to any statement made by him under said provision.—U. S. v. Cameron, 282 F. 684.

(Ala.App.1920) Under Code 1907, § 7543, the essentials to a conviction for perjury are that a lawful oath was administered by an officer having authority, that defendant as a witness swore falsely as to a material matter involved in some judicial proceeding, and that such false swearing was willful and corruptly done.— Goolsby v. State, 86 So. 137, 17 Ala. App. 545.

(Ala.App.1924) To establish perjury, state must show cause in court of competent jurisdiction, trial thereof, and false swearing by defendant to matter charged.—Taylor v. State, 101 So. 93, 20 Ala. App. 133.

(Ark.1924) For defendant to be guilty of perjury in making affidavit for marriage license, it was not necessary, as required by his requested instruction, that the affidavit should have been read to or by him, if he knew that it contained the recital about which the clerk was inquiring—that the girl was 18 years old. —Cox v. State, 261 S. W. 303, 164 Ark. 126.

(Cal.App.1921) To sustain a charge of perjury, the false testimony must have been given in a judicial proceeding and have been material to a valid issue properly made therein.—Ex parte Clark, 202 P. 50, 54 Cal. App. 507.

(Cal.App.1921) In an action of ejectment, where the complaint did not allege a lease of the land in question to defendant, a verified answer, admitting a lease from plaintiff to defendant, is not perjury.—Youdall v. Kaufman, 203 P. 448, 55 Cal. App. 363.

(Ill.1916) At common law, perjury was not a felony.—People v. Ashbrook, 114 N. E. 922, 276 Ill. 382.

(Ill.1920) "Perjury" is willfully, corruptly, and falsely testifying in a matter material to the issue or point in question. The testimony must be known to the witness to be false, and must be intended to mislead the court or jury. —People v. Glenn, 128 N. E. 532, 294 Ill. 333.

(Ind.1923) Testimony before a grand jury investigating a murder case, in answer to questions as to who fired certain pistol shots to the effect that accused was at another place when the shots were fired, held in effect a negative answer to the question and the subject of perjury, under Burns' Ann. St. 1914, § 2375, although the false statements were voluntarily made.—State v. Kellis, 141 N. E. 337, 193 Ind. 619.

(Ky.1917) Common-law perjury consists of willful giving under oath in a judicial proceeding, or in course of justice, false testimony material to issue.—Commonwealth v. Hinkle, 197 S. W. 455, 177 Ky. 22.

False swearing, under Ky. St. § 1174, is distinct from common-law crime of perjury, and statutory elements must exist.—Id.

(Mich.1924) To justify conviction of perjury, oath and facts sworn to must be material.— People v. Almashy, 201 N. W. 231, 229 Mich. 227.

(N.Y.App.Div.1919) Necessary elements of the crime of perjury by testifying falsely before a grand jury are that defendant should have taken an oath in a proceeding before one authorized to administer it, should have given testimony material in the proceeding, should have stated matter as true which he knew to be false, and such falsehood must have been willful and of his knowledge.—People v. Goodheim, 176 N. Y. S. 468, 188 App. Div. 148, 37 N. Y. Cr. R. 541.

(N.Y.App.Div.1919) To constitute the crime of perjury, under Penal Law, § 1620, not only must the testimony be false, but the witness must know it to be false, and must testify willfully and with a criminal intent.—People v. Redmond, 178 N. Y. S. 120, 189 App. Div. 96.

(N.Y.Sup.1916) To establish perjury it must appear that false testimony was knowingly and willfully given concerning material matter under investigation in a judicial or other proceeding authorized by law.—People v. Osborne, 158 N. Y. S. 330.

(N.Y.Sup.1924) For all practical purposes, the only legal punishment for marriage of parties under age is that which may be imposed under Domestic Relations Laws, § 16, on the person making the false statement or affidavit for the purpose of procuring a license.—Kellogg v. Kellogg, 203 N. Y. S. 757, 122 Misc. Rep. 734.

(Ohio,1922) Secretary of a building and loan association organized under Gen. Code, § 9643, who knowingly and willfully made a false statement under oath with reference to the assets and liabilities of the association in report to inspector of building and loan associations under sections 682, 683, held guilty of perjury under section 12842, even if it be assumed that the secretary came within the provisions of section 13190, prescribing penalty where "a member of a board of directors of a building and loan association" makes a false report or statement.—State v. Williams, 135 N. E. 651, 104 Ohio St. 232.

(Okl.Cr.App.1923) The material inquiries in a prosecution for perjury are: Did the party make an oath to testify, declare, depose, or certify truly before any competent tribunal, officer, or person, and did such person willfully and contrary to such oath state a material matter which he knew to be false, under Comp. St. 1921, § 1628?—Campbell v. State, 214 P. 738, 23 Okl. Cr. 250.

(Okl.Cr.App.1924) To constitute perjury the statement must not only be false, but the person making it must have known it to be false, or must have made it as unqualifiedly true without honestly believing it to be true.—Downard v. State, 223 P. 718.

⬅2. Statutory provisions.

Intoxicating liquor regulations, see Intoxicating Liquors, ⬅18.

(U.S.C.C.A.N.Y.1925) False swearing in bankruptcy proceedings is "perjury," within the meaning of Criminal Code, § 125 (Comp. St. § 10295); Bankruptcy Act, § 29b (Comp. St. § 9613), merely changing the punishment for perjury committed in, or in relation to, bankruptcy proceedings.—Hammer v. U. S., 6 F. (2d) 786, affirming judgment (D. C. 1924) U. S. v. Hammer, 299 F. 1011.

(La.1921) Act No. 166 of 1920, § 10, re-enacting Act No. 195 of 1916, § 28, relating to oaths to persons claiming the right to register as voters, and punishing perjury in relation thereto, does not, in providing that "unless otherwise provided for" it should be deemed a felony and punished as prescribed therein, have the effect of a saving clause so as to continue in force the old section for the punishment of offenses thereunder, but its purpose is to serve as an exception to the general penalty of five years' hard labor prescribed by Act No. 18 of 1888, for perjury, denounced by the old section, by preserving such special penalties as may have been provided for special instances, and the act of 1920, thus being without a saving clause, and increasing the minimum, and reducing the maximum, penalty prescribed by the old section, and changing the imprisonment to with or without hard labor repealed such old section by a general repealing clause as to all conflicting laws.—State v. Thomas, 89 So. 887, 149 La. 654.

(La.1925) Acts 1924, No. 198, providing for examination of judgment debtors in matters pertaining to their estates, and that a debtor

1916

SECOND

DECENNIAL EDITION

OF THE

AMERICAN DIGEST

A COMPLETE DIGEST OF ALL REPORTED
CASES FROM 1906 TO 1916

VOL. 17

NEGLIGENCE — PLEA

ST. PAUL
WEST PUBLISHING CO.
1921

Commitment of witness for perjury in presence of jury, see Criminal Law, ⚒658.

Conspiracy to commit, or procure commission of offense, see Conspiracy, ⚒34, 43(4, 6, 10), 45, 48.

Contempt, see Contempt, ⚒3, 13, 16, 36, 52, 60(3); in bankruptcy proceedings, see Bankruptcy, ⚒241(1), 486.

Continuance, see Criminal Law, ⚒595(4); suit by attorney after knowledge of client's attempt to recover on perjured testimony as malpractice, see Attorney and Client, ⚒42, 53(2).

Contracts inducing or requiring commission, validity, see Contracts, ⚒113(1), 129(2).

Creditors' suit, defenses, judgment obtained by perjury, see Creditors' Suit, ⚒18.

Disbarment for, see Attorney and Client, ⚒39, 42, 58.

Discovery to show perjury in verification of complaint, see Discovery, ⚒43.

District and prosecuting attorneys, duty to prosecute person committing perjury, see District and Prosecuting Attorneys, ⚒1.

Divorce, collateral attack on judgment or decree, see Divorce, ⚒168; opening or vacating decree, see Divorce, ⚒165(3), opening or vacating decree, see Divorce, ⚒165(5½).

Execution, against the person, false swearing in proceeding for discharge, see Execution, ⚒451; supplementary proceedings, false swearing on examination, see Execution, ⚒417.

Extraditability, see Extradition, ⚒32.

Foreign judgment, impeaching on account of, see Judgment, ⚒820.

Former jeopardy, see Criminal Law, ⚒170, 196, 200(1).

Instructions as to credibility of witnesses, see Criminal Law, ⚒785(15, 16).

Judgment, collateral attack on account of, see Judgment, ⚒512; effect of entry of satisfaction, see Judgment, ⚒899; equitable relief against on account of, see Judgment, ⚒444, 456(1); ground for action to review judgment, see Judgment, ⚒335(2); ground for vacation, see Judgment, ⚒386(7); impeach-

ing foreign judgment, see Judgment, ⚒820; opening on account of, see Judgment, ⚒376.

Jury, conviction for perjury as disqualification for jury duty, see Jury, ⚒45.

Libelous imputations, see Libel and Slander, ⚒7(14), 103.

Malicious prosecution, see Malicious Prosecution, ⚒3; burden of proof, see Malicious Prosecution, ⚒56; want of probable cause, see Malicious Prosecution, ⚒18(1, 2), 21, 24(4).

Naturalization proceedings, see Aliens, ⚒71½, 72.

New trial, causing arrest of party for perjury in presence of jury as ground, see New Trial, ⚒27; consideration of question of perjury in effort to obtain, see Criminal Law, ⚒959; ground for new trial, see Criminal Law, ⚒921, 942; New Trial, ⚒30, 90, 100.

Preliminary complaint, see Criminal Law, ⚒211(4).

Preliminary examination, see Criminal Law, ⚒230, 238.

Proceedings against witnesses for perjury on criminal trial, see Criminal Law, ⚒658.

Public lands, false affidavit under public land laws, see Public Lands, ⚒21; ground for equitable relief to claimant of public lands, see Public Lands, ⚒106(3).

Right to have charge submitted to grand jury before whom perjury was claimed to have been committed, see Criminal Law, ⚒576(1).

Slanderous imputations, see Libel and Slander, ⚒7(14), 103.

Supplementary proceedings, false swearing on examination, see Execution, ⚒417.

Torts, see Torts, ⚒13.

Vacating judgment or decree on account of, see Divorce, ⚒165(3, 5½); Judgment, ⚒376.

Weight and sufficiency of evidence in criminal prosecutions where witness subsequently states that the testimony was perjured, see Criminal Law, ⚒553.

Willful false testimony causing defeat of action, as creating civil liability against witness, see Torts, ⚒13.

Witnesses, competency as affected by conviction, see Witnesses, ⚒48(1, 3).

I. OFFENSES AND RESPONSIBILITY THEREFOR.

Different offenses in same transaction, see Criminal Law, ⚒29.

Infant, capacity to commit crime, see Infants, ⚒66.

⚒1. Nature and elements of offenses in general.

See 39 Cent. Dig. Perj. § 1.

(U.S.D.C.Neb.1906) To constitute perjury, the party charged must take an oath before some competent tribunal or officer that he will testify, declare, depose, or certify truly that his written testimony, declaration, or certificate by him subscribed was true, when in fact some material matter so testified, declared, or certified by him was false and untrue, and known by him at the time of taking such oath to have been false and untrue.—United States v. Richards, 149 F. 443.

(Del.Gen.Sess.1908) Perjury is an offense at common law, and consists of willfully, absolutely, and falsely swearing to a material matter in issue, where a lawful oath was administered in a judicial proceeding or in due course of justice.—State v. Shaffner, 69 A. 1004, 6 Pennewill, 576.

(Del.Gen.Sess.1910) The offense of perjury is committed when a lawful oath is administered in some judicial proceeding or in due course of justice to a person who swears willfully, abso-

lutely and falsely in a matter material to the issue or point in question.—State v. Rash, 78 A. 405, 2 Boyce, 77.

(Del.Gen.Sess.1910) Perjury at common law is committed when a lawful oath is administered in some judicial proceeding or in due course of justice to a person who swears willfully, absolutely, and falsely in a matter material to the issue or point in question.—State v. Thomas, 78 A. 640, 2 Boyce, 20.

(Ga.App.1913) That a witness has made other knowingly false statements under the same oath does not create new offenses, though the concurrence of other similar false statements may supply ground for a heavier penalty than would otherwise have been imposed.—Black v. State, 79 S. E. 173, 13 Ga. App. 541.

Perjury consists in knowingly, willfully, and falsely testifying to a material matter in a judicial proceeding, and the gist of the offense is the disregard of the oath taken; and the offense is complete if there be one false statement made with intent to conceal the truth.—Id.

(Ky.1907) It is only necessary to show, in order to convict defendant of perjury under Ky. St. 1903, § 1174, that the false statement was willfully made with a knowledge of its falsity on a subject as to which he might have been legally sworn, and that the oath was legally administered.—Stamper v. Commonwealth, 100 S. W. 286, 30 Ky. Law Rep. 992.

For earlier cases in First Decennial or cases in later Digests, see same topic and Key-Number.

51

1906

DECENNIAL EDITION

OF THE

AMERICAN DIGEST

A COMPLETE DIGEST OF ALL REPORTED CASES FROM 1897 TO 1906

VOL. 16

PENALTIES—RAILROAD LAND GRANTS

ST. PAUL
WEST PUBLISHING CO.
1910

Cross-References.

As bar to right to obtain divorce, see Divorce, § 10.
Civil liability for perjury, see Torts, § 13.
Continuance of criminal prosecution to procure testimony of one appealing from conviction of, see Criminal Law, § 589 (1).
Constituting contempt of court, see Contempt, §§ 13, 16, 60 (3).
Criminal liability for suppression of evidence and intimidation of witnesses, see Obstructing Justice, § 4.
Definition in instructions, see Criminal Law, § 800 (4).
Ground for collateral attack on judgment, see Judgment, § 512.
Ground for equitable relief against judgment, see Judgment, § 444.
Ground for equitable relief to claimant of public lands, see Public Lands, § 106 (3).
Ground for impeaching foreign judgment, see Judgment, § 820.
Ground for new trial, see Criminal Law, §§ 935 (1), 942 (1).
Ground for opening or vacating judgment, see Criminal Law, § 998; Judgment, § 376.
Ground for refusal of discharge in bankruptcy, see Bankruptcy, § 408 (1–5).
Ground for refusal of discharge of insolvent, see Insolvency, § 150.
Instructions as to credibility of witnesses, see Criminal Law, § 785 (15, 16).
Liability for false imprisonment of person instigating prosecution for perjury, see False Imprisonment, § 7 (4).
Liability for malicious prosecution dependent on probable cause for institution of prosecution, see Malicious Prosecution, § 18 (2).
Libelous and slanderous imputations, see Libel and Slander, § 7 (14).
Power of grand jury to indict witness in proceedings before them for perjury, see Grand Jury, § 26.
Proceedings against witnesses for perjury on criminal trial, see Criminal Law, § 658.

I. OFFENSES AND RESPONSIBILITY THEREFOR.

Merger of offenses, see Criminal Law, § 30.

§ 1. Nature and elements of offenses in general.
See 39 Cent. Dig. Perj. § 1.

[a] (Ind. 1831)
If a witness, with an intention to deceive the jury swear so as to make an impression on their minds that a fact material in the cause is different from what it really is, and from what he knows it to be, he is guilty of perjury.—Scott v. Mortsinger, 2 Blackf. 454.

[b] (Ky. 1891)
False swearing is a statutory offense entirely distinct from the common-law crime of perjury, and not included in the latter.—Commonwealth v. Scowden, 92 Ky. 120, 17 S. W. 205, 13 Ky. Law Rep. 404.

[c] (Mass. 1847)
The crime of perjury is the taking of a willful false oath by one who, being lawfully required to depose the truth in any judicial proceeding, swears absolutely in a matter material to the point in question.—Commonwealth v. Pollard, 53 Mass. (12 Metc.) 225.

[d] (Mich. 1872)
Perjury is committed "when a lawful oath is ministered by any that hath authority, to any person, in any judicial proceeding, who sweareth absolutely and falsely in any matter material to the issue or cause in question."—People v. Fox, 25 Mich. 492.

[e] (N. Y. O. & T. 1873)
To make out a case of perjury, it is necessary that the people allege and prove that there was a legal proceeding in which it was proper, competent, and necessary to administer an oath, and that an oath was administered, and that the person to whom it was administered testified willfully and corruptly to that which was false, and that it was matter material to the issues to be determined on such trial.—People v. Pearsall, 46 How. Prac. 121.

[f] (Tex. Cr. App. 1905)
In a prosecution for carrying a pistol, testimony by defendant that he did not have in his possession or on his person any pistol at the time alleged in the indictment is a sufficient basis for an indictment for perjury; the use of the disjunctive not rendering the statement duplicitous.—Trevinio v. State, 88 S. W. 356, 48 Tex. Cr. R. 350.

§ 2. Statutory provisions.
See 39 Cent. Dig. Perj. § 2.
Offense against state or United States, see Criminal Law, § 16.

[a] (N. Y. 1903)
Pen. Code, § 96, provides that a person who swears that any affidavit or other writing by him subscribed is true, on any occasion in which an oath is required by law, or is necessary for the prosecution or defense of a private right or for the end of public justice, and who willfully deposes falsely, or states in his affidavit any matter to be true which he knows to be false, is guilty of perjury. Held to include any and every oath or affidavit required by the laws of any other state, under the general rule of comity which exists between states. Order (1902) 79 N. Y. S. 340, 77 App. Div. 396, 17 N. Y. Cr. R. 150, which reversed order (Sup. 1902) 76 N. Y. S. 953, 38 Misc. Rep. 67, affirmed.—People v. Martin, 67 N. E. 589, 175 N. Y. 315, 96 Am. St. Rep 628.

[b] (Okl. 1894)
A prosecution for perjury committed in the United States land office is brought under Rev. St. U. S. § 5392, defining the offense, and prescribing its punishment.—Peters v. United States, 37 P. 1081, 2 Okl. 138.

[c] (Tex. Cr. App. 1902)
Pen. Code, § 209, provides the punishment for deliberately or willfully, under oath or affirmation legally administered, making a false statement by declaration or affidavit which is not required by law, or made in the course of a judicial proceeding. Const. art. 1, § 5, declares that no person shall be disqualified to give evidence in any of the courts on account of his religious opinions, but that all oaths or affirmations shall be taken subject to the pains and penalties of perjury. Held, that the constitution refers to witnesses while giving evidence, and not to false swearing, within Pen. Code, § 209, and the statute is not unconstitutional.—Campbell v. State, 68 S. W. 513, 43 Tex. Cr. R. 602.

[d] (Tex. Cr. App. 1902)
Pen. Code, § 209, provides the punishment for deliberately or willfully, under oath or affirmation legally administered, making a false statement by declaration or affidavit which is not required by law, or made in the course of a judicial proceeding; article 3, Rev. Civ. St., provides that all oaths and affirmations shall

---

Main titles, divisions, and section NUMBERS in this Digest and in later Am. Digests agree exactly.

53

CENTURY EDITION

OF THE

AMERICAN DIGEST

A COMPLETE DIGEST OF ALL REPORTED AMERICAN CASES FROM THE EARLIEST TIMES TO 1896

VOL. 39
Payment—Pleading

ST. PAUL
WEST PUBLISHING CO.
1903

PERJURY.

I. OFFENSES AND RESPONSIBILITY THEREFOR.

(A) IN GENERAL.

NATURE AND ELEMENTS OF OFFENSES IN
GENERAL, § 1.
STATUTORY PROVISIONS, § 2.
INTENT, § 3.

§ 1. Nature and elements of offenses in general.

[a] (U. S. 1894) Rev. St. § 5392 [U. S. Comp. St. 1901, p. 3653], defining the crime of perjury, is not confined in its operation to places within the exclusive jurisdiction of the United States, but is of universal application within the territorial limits thereof; and the crime is punishable in the district court of the district in which it is committed.—Caha v. United States, 152 U. S. 211, 14 Sup. Ct. 513, 38 L. Ed. 415.

[b] (Ala. 1870) Perjury is a corrupt, willful, false oath, taken in a judicial proceeding, in regard to a matter or thing material to a point involved in the proceeding. This oath must be taken before some officer or court having authority to administer it, and he must confine his action to the authority given. It is competent to show that the accused might have been led into a mistake; then the oath, though untruthful, could not have been perjury.—Hood v. State, 44 Ala. 81.

[bb] (Fla. 1876) It is not sufficient, in a case of perjury, for the court to charge the jury "that if they believed, from the testimony, that the accused took the oath, and that it was false, he was guilty." The court should charge that they must find that the accused took a willfully false oath, and that it must be so taken in relation to matter material to the issue, in order to make him subject to the punishment provided for perjury.—Miller v. State, 15 Fla. 577.

[c] (Ga. 1822) Perjury is felony in this state, though it is not so at common law.—A. v. B., R. M. Charlt. 228.

[d] (Ill. 1885) Although a question put to a witness may assume that which is incorrect, he is bound, so far as he undertakes to answer it, to speak the truth.—Mackin v. People, 115 Ill. 312, 3 N. E. 222.

[e] (Ky. 1859) Rev. St. p. 252, art. 8, § 2, defines and creates an offense totally distinct from that of perjury at common law. To constitute the offense, it is not necessary either that the false oath should be taken in a matter judicially pending at the time, or in a matter material to any point in question, but it is complete if the false oath be taken knowingly and willfully, on a subject on which the party could be legally sworn, and before a person legally authorized to administer the oath.—Commonwealth v. Powell, 59 Ky. (2 Metc.) 10.

[f] (Ky. 1859) Perjury at common law is the "taking of a willful false oath by one who, being lawfully sworn by a competent court to depose the truth in any judicial proceeding, swears absolutely and falsely, in a matter material to the point in issue, whether he believed or not."—Commonwealth v. Powell, 59 Ky. (2 Metc.) 10.

[g] (Mo. 1835) Falsely denying a fact on the direct examination is not the less perjury because the witness confesses to it on the cross-examination.—Martin v. Miller, 4 Mo. 47, 28 Am. Dec. 342.

[h] (Mo. 1882) Under Rev. St. § 1421, providing that every person who shall, before any officer authorized to administer oaths, make a false affidavit, etc., it is not necessary that the false oath should be taken in a judicial proceeding pending at the time, or in a matter material to any point in question, but the offense is complete if the false oath was taken knowingly and willingly on a subject on which the party could be legally sworn, and before a person legally authorized to administer oaths.—State v. Boland, 12 Mo. App. 74.

[i] (N. J. 1850) The act relative to oaths and affidavits makes false swearing in any lawful oath taken in pursuance of that act to be perjury.—State v. Dayton, 23 N. J. Law (3 Zab.) 49, 53 Am. Dec. 270.

[j] (N. Y. 1857) Perjury in a proceeding for naturalization in a state court is an offense against the general government, and is punishable by proceeding in the courts of the United States and not in the state courts.—People v. Sweetman, 3 Parker, Cr. R. 358.

[k] (N. C. 1819) Perjury committed on the trial of an issue consists of giving false evidence to the jury in a material point in issue.—State v. Witherow, 7 N. C. 153.

[l] (Ohio, 1896) Where a witness knowingly makes contradictory and irreconcilable statements under oath before different grand juries, he commits perjury.—In re Commissioners of Franklin County, 7 Ohio N. P. 450, 5 Ohio S. & C. P. Dec. 691.

[m] (Ohio, 1896) To constitute perjury, the person testifying must willfully, corruptly, and contrary to his oath state a falsehood as to some material matter which he does not believe to be true.—In re Commissioners of Franklin County, 7 Ohio N. P. 450, 5 Ohio S. & C. P. Dec. 691.

[n] (Pa. 1844) To sustain a prosecution for perjury, it must appear that the oath was false, the intention willful, the proceedings judicial, the party lawfully sworn, the assertion absolute, and the falsehood material to the matter in question.—Commonwealth v. Knutz, 4 Pa. Law J. 163.

[o] (Pa. 1879) Perjury is where a lawful oath is administered in some judicial proceeding to a person who swears knowingly, willfully, falsely, and corruptly, to a matter material to the point or question in issue.—Commonwealth v. Williams, 1 Lack. Leg. Rec. 246.

§ 2. Statutory provisions.

[a] (Ky. 1891) Though the facts charged constitute perjury at common law, the state may elect to proceed by indictment for false swearing, under Gen. St. c. 29, art. 8, § 2, providing that if, in any matter judicially pending, or on any subject in which he can be legally sworn, or on which he is required to be sworn, any

2. American Jurisprudence 2d

American Jurisprudence

American Jurisprudence 2d (Am Jur 2d) is a comprehensive legal encyclopedia containing textual statements of law, alphabetically arranged under 436 topics or chapters. Am Jur 2d articles collect, examine and summarize the broad principles of American law, and at the same time provide direct leads to supporting cases, related annotations, forms, proofs and trial techiques.

Am Jur 2d

502 N.Y.S. 2nd 325

Am Jur 2d Problem

(130mrsc. 2d. 398.)

AIDS. school.

A third grade girl is diagnosed as having the AIDS virus. Shortly after disclosure of this information to the public school principal, the local school authoriities notify her parents that she is prohibited from attending the school. The parents file charges against the school, claiming that their daughter is unjustly being denied access to public education. The school responds by saying that they are seeking to protect the other children from the threat of infection. Find cases that discuss the issue.

1986 Dist. 27 Community Sch bd. by Granirer
V Bd of Ed. City of NY   V - Bd of ed. of city of NY

Worksheet

29 USC P. 794

Parties:

Places and Things: Supreme Court - Queens, N.Y. (pres
Dist. 27 Comm. Sch bd, - GRANIRER -
Dist 27 Comm Sch bd -

Basis of Action or Issue:
Student @ AIDS

Defense: Violation Rehabilitation act
not classifud as a Communicable desease -

Relief Sought:

McKinney's #601
ed. Law

KeyCite - 502 N.Y.S. 2d. 325

58

American Jurisprudence

SECOND EDITION

A MODERN COMPREHENSIVE TEXT STATEMENT
OF AMERICAN LAW

STATE AND FEDERAL

COMPLETELY REVISED AND REWRITTEN
IN THE LIGHT OF MODERN AUTHORITIES AND DEVELOPMENTS
BY THE EDITORIAL STAFF OF THE PUBLISHERS

GENERAL INDEX

2001 EDITION

S–Z
POPULAR NAMES TABLE

Bancroft-Whitney • Clark Boardman Callaghan
Lawyers Cooperative Publishing • WESTLAW® • West Publishing

SCHOOL BUSES—Cont'd

Handicapped persons. **Americans with Disabilities Act** (this index)

Insurance, **Ins § 666**

Mandamus, **Mand § 122, 240**

Municipal, County, School, and State Tort Liability (this index)

Nuisances, **Nuis § 184**

Parochial schools, **Sch § 374-376**

Pensions for busdrivers, **Pens § 1133**

Persons entitled to transportation, **Sch § 266**

Power to provide transportation, **Sch § 263**

Zoning and planning, **Zoning § 226, 409, 422**

SCHOOLS

Colleges and Universities (this index)

SCHOOLS AND EDUCATION

Generally, **Sch § 1-412**

Absence or presence
  attendance by students, below
  teachers and other employees, below

Abuse of children, actions against private schools for failure to report child abuse, **Sch § 406**

Achievement tests, **Sch § 241**

Actions and remedies
  administrative officers and boards, below
  funds, **Sch § 129-133**
  legality of organization of school district, **Sch § 46-50**
  private schools, below
  property and buildings, actions to preserve or protect, **Sch § 81**
  religion, **Sch § 368**
  sue or be sued, power of school district to, **Sch § 20**
  teachers and other employees, below
  transportation of students, failure to provide, **Sch § 269**

Administrative officers and boards
  generally, **Sch § 59-79**
  actions and remedies
    powers and duties, **Sch § 76**
    right to office, **Sch § 67**
  boundaries of school district, change of consent of board or residents, **Sch § 37**
  discretion of officers, **Sch § 38**
  county officer or employee, superintendent of school as, **Mun Corp § 235**
  courts, control by, **Sch § 75, 76, 79**
  declaratory judgments, board of education, **Decl J § 101-103, 120**
  de facto officers, **Sch § 66**
  definitions, **Admin L § 27**
  delegation of legislative authority to officers or boards, **Sch § 35**
  discretion of school authorities, board, or officers, below
  dismissal of school employees, **Sch § 205**
  election of officers by school board, **Sch § 72**
  eligibility, **Sch § 61, 62**
  incompatible offices, **Sch § 62**
  judicial review, **Admin L § 447, 469, 624**
  limitations on powers, **Sch § 74, 78**

SCHOOLS AND EDUCATION —Cont'd

Administrative officers and boards—Cont'd
  malicious prosecution, immunity of school official, **Mal Pros § 69**
  meetings
    generally, **Admin L § 102; Sch § 68-72**
    election of officers by school board, **Sch § 72**
    evidence, **Sch § 71**
    minutes, **Sch § 70**
    open meeting laws, **Sch § 69**
    records, **Sch § 70**
    sunshine laws, **Sch § 69**
  minutes, **Sch § 70**
  municipal corporations, board of education, **Mun Corp § 14, 713, 780**
  nature of office, **Sch § 59**
  open meeting laws, **Sch § 69**
  post office, **Post Off § 155**
  powers and duties, **Sch § 73-76**
  property and buildings, nature of interest of school board in, **Sch § 83**
  quo warranto, proceedings, challenging exercise of power by education board of municipality, **Quo War § 47**
  records, **Sch § 70**
  removal, **Sch § 64**
  resignation, **Sch § 64**
  right to office, remedies, **Sch § 67**
  rules and regulations, **Admin L § 220, 243; Sch § 77-79**
  selection, **Sch § 60**
  sunshine laws, **Sch § 69**
  teachers and other employees, below
  tenure, attainment of, **Sch § 197**
  term of office, **Sch § 63**
  tort liability. **Municipal, County, School, and State Tort Liability** (this index)
  vacancies, **Sch § 65**
  witnesses, **Witn § 184**

Admission
  Mandamus (this index)

Adoption, education of parent
  adoption without parent's consent, **Adopt § 87**
  consent to adoption, revocation or withdrawal of, **Adopt § 108**

Ad valorem taxes, **Sch § 101**

Adverse possession, **Adv Poss § 183, 273**

Adviser
  investment adviser or broker-dealer as including teacher, **Sec Reg St § 16**

Age of children, **Sch § 250**

Agriculture (this index)

AIDS, exclusion of students with, **Sch § 317**

Alcoholic beverages. Intoxicating liquors, below

Alternative Dispute Resolution (this index)

Alternatives to public school, generally, **Sch § 254**

Amendment of tenure statutes, **Sch § 188**

Americans with Disabilities Act (ADA), interscholastic sports, **Sch § 280-282**

Americans with Disabilities Act (this index)

Animals
  research, **Agri § 24**
  Riding School or Academy (this index)

SCHOOLS AND EDUCATION —Cont'd

Animals—Cont'd
  veterinarians, educational requirements for licenses, **Veteriniar § 3**

Annexation of school district, **Sch § 41**

Apparel. Clothing, below

Appeal and error
  administrative officers and boards, **Admin L § 447, 469, 624**

Appeal and review
  Individuals with Disabilities Education Act (IDEA), **Sch § 351, 352**
  school districts, legality of organization of, **Sch § 47, 48**

Appearance of students, **Sch § 287-289**

Apportionment or distribution of funds
  generally, **Sch § 109-117**
  attendance, enrollment, or pupil population, apportionment of funds based on, **Sch § 116, 117**
  conditional entitlement to funds, **Sch § 114**
  constitutional law, **Sch § 112**
  other district, attendance of pupils residing in, **Sch § 117**
  state funds, right of district or school to share in, **Sch § 113-115**
  uniform distribution, **Sch § 110, 111**

Appropriate education requirements, **Sch § 344**

Appropriations
  generally, **Sch § 106-108**
  power to appropriate, **Sch § 106**
  reduction of funds, **Sch § 108**
  revenues from which appropriations may be made, **Sch § 107**

Argument of counsel referring to wealth or poverty, **Trial § 673**

Arm bands and buttons, **Sch § 289**

Assault and Battery (this index)

Assignment or transfer. Teachers and other employees, below

Association, freedom of, **Const L § 557**

Associations and clubs
  employment contracts, incorporation of agreements with teacher associations, **Sch § 157**
  Fraternities or Sororities (this index)
  interscholastic sports, **Sch § 279**

Athletics. Sports and athletics, below

Attachment and garnishment, **Attach § 83**

Attendance by students
  age of children, **Sch § 250**
  alternatives to public school, generally, **Sch § 254**
  apportionment of funds based on attendance, **Sch § 116, 117**
  charitable institution, child residing in, **Sch § 248**
  compulsory attendance, **Sch § 253-262**
  exclusion of students, below
  health, below
  home schools, below
  kind of education, **Sch § 243**
  leaving school grounds, **Sch § 275**
  married students, **Sch § 251**
  noncompliance with compulsory attendance, **Sch § 258-262**

For assistance using this Index, call 1-800-328-4880

American Jurisprudence

SECOND EDITION

A MODERN COMPREHENSIVE TEXT STATEMENT OF
AMERICAN LAW

STATE AND FEDERAL

COMPLETELY REVISED AND REWRITTEN
IN THE LIGHT OF MODERN AUTHORITIES AND DEVELOPMENTS

VOLUME 68

SALES AND USE TAXES

TO

SEARCHES AND SEIZURES

2000

WEST GROUP

Bancroft-Whitney • Clark Boardman Callaghan
Lawyers Cooperative Publishing • WESTLAW® • West Publishing

is infected with a contagious disease[90] or has been dangerously exposed to such a disease.[91]

§ 317. —Children infected with the AIDS virus

Acquired Immune Deficiency Syndrome (AIDS) disables victims of the disease by collapsing their immune systems, making them unable to fight infection.[92] State education authorities, rather than local school authorities, are the appropriate parties to promulgate regulations concerning the right of AIDS-infected children to attend public school, since the state's power to regulate on the issue, inferable from its broad grant of authority to supervise the schools, pre-empts any rights of local authorities under their statutory discretion to exclude children from school to prevent the spread of contagious disease.[93]

◆ *Caution:* State statutes and local health regulations concerning contagious diseases in general, which make no specific reference to AIDS, do not apply to the decision whether AIDS-infected students should be allowed to attend public school.[94]

Procedures for determining whether AIDS-infected children should be excluded from a public school have withstood a due process challenge, one court having upheld the constitutionality of a plan which provided for an impartial decision by a medical panel, proper notice, and the opportunity to call and cross-examine witnesses.[95] However, distinguishing between students known to be infected with AIDS and students who were unidentified carriers of AIDS-related complex or asymptomatic carriers is constitutionally unacceptable since the proposed exclusion from public school of only the known AIDS-infected children constitutes an equal protection violation.[96]

◆ *Practice Guide:* Numerous organizations, both medical and educational, have formulated guidelines on when AIDS carriers should be segregated from the rest of the population. In cases concerning the right of a student with AIDS to attend school, courts have received evidence of the guidelines

90. Kenney v. Gurley, 208 Ala. 623, 95 So. 34, 26 A.L.R. 813 (1923); Nutt v. Board of Education of City of Goodland, Sherman County, 128 Kan. 507, 278 P. 1065 (1929).

As to the right to public education, generally, see §§ 242 et seq.

Forms: Answer—Defense—School district providing home teaching to student with contagious or infectious disease pending determination whether student's attendance at school would be danger to others. 22 Am Jur Pl & Pr Forms (Rev), Schools, Form 182.

91. Bright v. Beard, 132 Minn. 375, 157 N.W. 501 (1916).

92. Board of Educ. of City of Plainfield, Union County v. Cooperman, 105 N.J. 587, 523 A.2d 655, 38 Ed. Law Rep. 607, 60 A.L.R.4th 1 (1987).

Law Reviews: AIDS in public schools: Resolved issues and continuing controversy, 24 J Law and Educ 1:69 (1995).

Students with AIDS: Protecting an infected child's right to a classroom education and

developing a school's AIDS policy, 40 S Dakota LR 1:72 (1995).

93. Board of Educ. of City of Plainfield, Union County v. Cooperman, 105 N.J. 587, 523 A.2d 655, 38 Ed. Law Rep. 607, 60 A.L.R.4th 1 (1987).

94. District 27 Community School Bd. by Granirer v. Board of Educ. of City of New York, 130 Misc. 2d 398, 502 N.Y.S.2d 325, 32 Ed. Law Rep. 740 (Sup. Ct. 1986).

95. Board of Educ. of City of Plainfield, Union County v. Cooperman, 105 N.J. 587, 523 A.2d 655, 38 Ed. Law Rep. 607, 60 A.L.R.4th 1 (1987).

Forms: Complaint, petition, or declaration—To enjoin expulsion of student who tested positive for AIDS virus—By guardian. 22 Am Jur Pl & Pr Forms (Rev), Schools, Form 177.

96. District 27 Community School Bd. by Granirer v. Board of Educ. of City of New York, 130 Misc. 2d 398, 502 N.Y.S.2d 325, 32 Ed. Law Rep. 740 (Sup. Ct. 1986).

537

formulated by the Centers for Disease Control[97] and various state or local educational bodies.[98]

Psychological evaluations of the student have also been admitted in evidence.[99]

X. COURSES OF INSTRUCTION; TEXTBOOKS [§§ 318-324]

A. COURSE OF INSTRUCTION [§§ 318-320]

Research References

20 USCA § 1232a
ALR Digest: Schools §§ 64-69
ALR Index: Curriculum; Schools and Education; Textbooks
West Digest, Schools ☞ 89.19, 163, 164

---

§ 318. Generally; power of state legislature

The fundamental power to select the system of instruction and course of study to be pursued in the public schools belongs to the legislature.[1] However, a state statute prohibiting any teacher in the state schools from teaching the Darwinian theory of evolution is contrary to the mandate of the First Amendment, and in violation of the Fourteenth Amendment, as conflicting with the constitutional prohibition of state laws respecting an establishment of religion or prohibiting the free exercise thereof.[2]

♦ *Observation:* A state statute that imposes a rigorous academic program on its students does not operate as a state mechanism for controlling the minds and speech of public school students, and does not facially violate the First Amendment, when the statute merely imposes an educational structure and philosophy on the public schools.[3]

97. Board of Educ. of City of Plainfield, Union County v. Cooperman, 105 N.J. 587, 523 A.2d 655, 38 Ed. Law Rep. 607, 60 A.L.R.4th 1 (1987).

98. Board of Educ. of City of Plainfield, Union County v. Cooperman, 105 N.J. 587, 523 A.2d 655, 38 Ed. Law Rep. 607, 60 A.L.R.4th 1 (1987).

99. Board of Educ. of City of Plainfield, Union County v. Cooperman, 105 N.J. 587, 523 A.2d 655, 38 Ed. Law Rep. 607, 60 A.L.R.4th 1 (1987); District 27 Community School Bd. by Granirer v. Board of Educ. of City of New York, 130 Misc. 2d 398, 502 N.Y.S.2d 325, 32 Ed. Law Rep. 740 (Sup. Ct. 1986).

1. Associated Schools of Independent Dist. No. 63 of Hector, Renville County v. School Dist. No. 83 of Renville County, 122 Minn. 254, 142 N.W. 325 (1913); Posey v. Board of Educ. of Buncombe County, 199 N.C. 306, 154 S.E. 393, 70 A.L.R. 1306 (1930); Mumme v. Marrs, 120 Tex. 383, 40 S.W.2d 31 (1931).

2. Epperson v. State of Ark., 393 U.S. 97, 89 S. Ct. 266, 21 L. Ed. 2d 228 (1968) (distinguished on other grounds by, Right To Choose v. Byrne, 165 N.J. Super. 443, 398 A.2d 587 (Ch. Div. 1979)) and (distinguished on other grounds by, Gartner v. U.S. Information Agency, 726 F. Supp. 1183 (S.D. Iowa 1989)) and (distinguished on other grounds by, International Paper Co. v. Inhabitants of Town of Jay, 736 F. Supp. 359, 134 L.R.R.M. (BNA) 2188, 115 Lab. Cas. (CCH) ¶ 10099 (D. Me. 1990)) and (declined to extend on other grounds by, Schmidling v. City of Chicago, 1 F.3d 494 (7th Cir. 1993)) and (distinguished on other grounds by, San Diego County Gun Rights Committee v. Reno, 98 F.3d 1121 (9th Cir. 1996)).

As to schools and the church-state relationship, generally, see §§ 354 et seq.

3. Tennison v. Paulus, 144 F.3d 1285 (9th Cir. 1998), cert. denied, 119 S. Ct. 800, 142 L. Ed. 2d 662 (U.S. 1999).

3. United States Code Annotated

U.S.C.A.

The United States Code Annotated is a helpful resource to find case law which interprets or defines federal law. The problem again assumes that you will isolate descriptive words, consult the U.S.C.A. indexing system, and locate a statute. The statute you locate has annotations to cases citing it which deal with your legal problem.

U.S.C.A.

U.S.C.A. Problem

A man is observed by government agents in his parked car talking on his car phone. Later, other cars were seen to drive up to his car and stop. The drivers received brown paper bags in exchange for money. The man was questioned and his car was searched. Cocaine, a controled substance, was found in the car.

Is there any authority in the U.S. Code for forfeiture of the vehicle?

Worksheet

Parties:

Places and Things:

Basis of Action or Issue:

Defense:

Relief Sought:

UNITED STATES CODE ANNOTATED

2000
GENERAL INDEX
D to E

DRINKING WATER—Cont'd
United States Embassies and Consulates, 22
§ 2670

DRIVE FOR TEEN EMPLOYMENT ACT
Generally, 29 §§ 201 nt, 213

DRIVE–BY SHOOTING PREVENTION ACT OF 1994
See Popular Name Table following

DRIVERS
Drivers' Licenses, generally, this index
Highways and Roads, this index
Labor and employment, exemption of employ-
ees employed as driver or driver's helper
making local deliveries, 29 § 213
Motor Vehicles, this index

DRIVERS' LICENSES
Alcohol traffic safety programs, suspension, 23
§ 408
Driving while intoxicated or under the influ-
ence,
Fines, penalties and forfeitures, 23 § 164
Fines, penalties and forfeitures,
Driving while intoxicated or under the influ-
ence, 23 § 164
Government property, management and dis-
posal of, motor vehicle pools, 40 § 491
Highways and roads, safety program, special
grant to State, driving under influence of
alcohol, State statute providing mandato-
ry suspension of, 23 § 408
Motor vehicle operators, implied consent for
certain test, effect of refusal, 18 § 3118
Repeat intoxicated driver law, 23 § 164
Revocation or suspension,
Driving while intoxicated or under the influ-
ence, countermeasures, 23 § 410
National Driver Register, 49 § 30302

DRIVER'S PRIVACY PROTECTION ACT OF 1994
See Popular Name Table following this index

**DRIVING WHILE INTOXICATED OR UN-
DER THE INFLUENCE**
Motor Vehicles, this index

DROPOUTS
Schools and School Districts, this index

DROUGHTS
Agricultural lands, grazing, adjustments, certif-
icates and certification, 7 § 1838
Boards and commissions, Policy Commission,
42 § 5121 nt
Cotton, acreage not planted,
Payments, producers, 7 § 1444
Price supports, 7 § 1444
Disaster relief and emergency assistance, 42
§ 5121 et seq.
Emergency crop loss assistance, payments, 7
§ 1421 nt
Floods and flood control, construction of wells
in drought areas, 33 § 701n
Grazing lands, reduction or refund, 43 § 315b

DROUGHTS—Cont'd
Income tax, special rule for proceeds from
livestock sold on account of, taxable year
of inclusion, 26 § 451
Indian lands, emergency livestock feed, dis-
tressed areas, Federal aid, delegation of
Presidential authority, 7 § 1427 nt, EON
11336
Irrigation and Reclamation, generally, this in-
dex
Labor and employment, closings or layoffs,
notice 29 § 2101 et seq.
Policy Commission, 42 § 5121 nt
Reports, Policy Commission, 42 § 5121 nt
Studies, Policy Commission, 42 § 5121 nt
Tobacco, emergency allotment leases and
transfers, Georgia, South Carolina, 7
§ 1314b
Water management, rural areas, 7 § 2204c
Weather, generally, this index
Wheat, marketing certificates, 7 § 1379c

DRUG ABUSE CONTROL AMENDMENTS OF 1965
See Popular Name Table following this index

DRUG ABUSE OFFICE AND TREATMENT ACT OF 1972
See Popular Name Table following this index

DRUG ABUSE TREATMENT TECHNICAL CORRECTIONS ACT OF 1989
See Popular Name Table following this index

**DRUG ABUSE TREATMENT WAITING PE-
RIOD REDUCTION AMENDMENTS OF 1990**
See Popular Name Table following this index

DRUG ADDICTS
Generally, 21 § 1101 et seq.; 42 § 257 et
seq.
Admissions,
District of Columbia, 42 § 260a
Probationers, hospitals, 42 § 259
Public Health Service hospitals, 42 § 260a
Voluntary patients, hospitals, 42 § 260
Advances,
Special project grants or contracts, 21
§ 1177
Advertisements,
Children and minors, 21 § 1801 et seq.
Aftercare, supervision, 42 § 257
Aged persons, applications, 21 § 1177
Aliens, removal, 8 § 1227
Applications,
Admissions, hospitals, 42 § 260
Aged persons, special consideration, special
project grants and contracts, 21 § 1177
Special project grants and contracts, criteria,
approval, 21 § 1177
Appropriations,
Abuse at workplace, 21 § 801 nt
Children and minors, media campaign, 21
§ 1804
District of Columbia, hospitals, 42 § 260a

DRUG ENFORCEMENT ADMINISTRATION
—Cont'd
Foreign language capabilities, employees, payment of bonuses for, 5 § 5541 nt
Funds, use, travel, expenses of State, criminal justice personnel attending meeting, at Federal Training Center, 42 § 3771 nt
Grades excepted from competitive service, positions in, 28 § 509 nt
Humanitarian expenses, appropriations, authorization, 28 § 509 nt
Informers, rewards, payments, advances, 21 § 886
Intelligence, Office of, Federal labor-management relations program, exclusions from, 5 § 7103 nt, EON 12171
Liabilities, civil and criminal, 21 § 885
Misuse of initials, DEA, 18 § 709 nt
Office of Inspections, portion of engaged in internal audit activities, transfer of functions to Inspector General of Justice Department, 5, Ap 3, § 9
Office of Planning and Evaluation, portion engaged in program review activities, transfer of functions to Inspector General of Justice Department, 5, Ap 3, § 9
Payments, advances, 21 § 886
Senior-level positions, 5 § 5376
Personnel research programs and demonstration projects, inapplicability of provisions to positions in, 5 § 4701
Positions,
    Maximum number, Presidential authority, 5 § 5108
    Vacancies, 28 § 509 nt
Reduction in rank or pay, 28 § 509 nt
Removal, 28 § 509 nt
Reports, undercover investigative operations closed in certain year, financial audit, contents, time, 28 § 533 nt
Robberies and burglaries involving controlled substances, belonging to, persons registered with, penalties, 18 § 2118
Rural crime and drug enforcement task forces, membership, 42 § 14081
Searches and seizures, 21 § 878
Secretary of State, assignment of agents abroad, 22 § 2656 nt
Southeast Asia, disclosure of information concerning POWs, MIAs, 50 § 435 nt
Declassification and release, 50 § 435 nt, EON 12812
Subpoenas, 21 § 878
Summons, 21 § 878
Suspension, positions in, 28 § 509 nt
Tort claims, foreign countries, payment, 21 § 904
Training and manpower development, State, local criminal justice personnel, prohibition, fees, reimbursement, 42 § 3771 nt
Treasury Department, Attorney General to direct advance of funds, 21 § 886
Undercover investigative operations,
    Closed in certain year, financial audit, submission of results, reports, 28 § 533 nt

DRUG ENFORCEMENT ADMINISTRATION
—Cont'd
Undercover investigative operations—Cont'd
Defined, financial audit of undercover investigative operations closed in certain year, 28 § 533 nt
Undercover operation, defined, financial audit of undercover investigative operations closed in certain year, 28 § 533 nt
Uniforms, allowances, appropriations as permitted utilization, 28 § 509 nt
Vacancies, positions in, 28 § 509 nt
Violations, enforcement proceedings, 21 § 883

DRUG EXPORT AMENDMENTS ACT OF 1986
See Popular Name Table following this index

DRUG FREE COMMUNITIES
Controlled Substances, this index

DRUG FREE COMMUNITIES ACT OF 1997
See Popular Name Table following this index

DRUG FREE MEDIA CAMPAIGN ACT OF 1998
Generally, 21 § 1801 et seq.

DRUG FREE PUBLIC HOUSING ACT OF 1988
See Popular Name Table following this index

DRUG FREE SCHOOLS AND COMMUNITIES ACT AMENDMENTS OF 1989
See Popular Name Table following this index

DRUG FREE SCHOOLS QUALITY ASSURANCE ACT
See Popular Name Table following this index

DRUG FREE TRUCK STOP ACT
See Popular Name Table following this index

DRUG FREE WORKPLACE ACT OF 1988
See Popular Name Table following this index

DRUG FREE WORKPLACE ACT OF 1998
See Popular Name Table following this index

DRUG INDUCED RAPE PREVENTION AND PUNISHMENT ACT OF 1996
See Popular Name Table following this index

DRUG INTERDICTION
Secretary of Defense, this index

DRUG LISTING ACT OF 1972
Generally, 21 §§ 301 nt, 331, 335, 360, 360 nt

DRUG POSSESSION PENALTY ACT OF 1986
Generally, 21 § 844

DRUG PRICE COMPETITION AND PATENT TERM RESTORATION ACT OF 1984
See Popular Name Table following this index

DRUGGISTS AND DRUG STORES
Pharmacists, generally, this index

UNITED STATES CODE ANNOTATED

TITLE 21

Food and Drugs

§§ 848 to End

Comprising All Laws of a General
and Permanent Nature
Under Arrangement of the Official Code of
the Laws of the United States
with
Annotations from Federal and State Courts

TITLES OF
UNITED STATES CODE
AND
UNITED STATES CODE ANNOTATED

---

1. General Provisions.
2. The Congress.
3. The President.
4. Flag and Seal, Seat of Government, and the States.
5. Government Organization and Employees.
6. Surety Bonds (*See Title 31, Money and Finance*).
7. Agriculture.
8. Aliens and Nationality.
9. Arbitration.
10. Armed Forces.
11. Bankruptcy.
12. Banks and Banking.
13. Census.
14. Coast Guard.
15. Commerce and Trade.
16. Conservation.
17. Copyrights.
18. Crimes and Criminal Procedure.
19. Customs Duties.
20. Education.
21. Food and Drugs.
22. Foreign Relations and Intercourse.
23. Highways.
24. Hospitals and Asylums.
25. Indians.
26. Internal Revenue Code.
27. Intoxicating Liquors.
28. Judiciary and Judicial Procedure.
29. Labor.
30. Mineral Lands and Mining.
31. Money and Finance.
32. National Guard.
33. Navigation and Navigable Waters.
34. Navy (*See Title 10, Armed Forces*).
35. Patents.
36. Patriotic Societies and National Observances, Ceremonies, and Organizations.
37. Pay and Allowances of the Uniformed Services.
38. Veterans' Benefits.
39. Postal Service.
40. Public Buildings, Property, and Works.
41. Public Contracts.
42. The Public Health and Welfare.
43. Public Lands.
44. Public Printing and Documents.
45. Railroads.
46. Shipping.
47. Telegraphs, Telephones, and Radiotelegraphs.
48. Territories and Insular Possessions.
49. Transportation.
50. War and National Defense.

II

INDEX TO

TITLE 21—FOOD AND DRUGS

References are to Sections

827

903

DRUG ADDICTS—Continued
Telecommunications,
 Children and minors, **21 § 1801 et seq.**
Television and radio,
 Children and minors, **21 § 1801 et seq.**
Underserved populations, consideration to applications for programs and
  projects aimed at, **21 § 1177**
Women, programs and projects for, special project grants and contracts, **21
 § 1177**

DRUG AND HOUSEHOLD SUBSTANCE MAILING ACT OF 1990
Postal Service, generally, this index

DRUG ENFORCEMENT ADMINISTRATION
Administrative inspection warrants, **21 § 878**
Administrator,
 Joint Federal Task Force on Illegal Drug Laboratories, **21 § 801 nt**
 United States attorneys, enforcement proceedings, notice to potential de-
  fendant, **21 § 883**
Advances, funds, enforcement, **21 § 886**
Arrest warrants, **21 § 878**
Defined, **21 § 802**
Diversion Control Fee Account, operation of diversion control programs, **21
 § 886a**
Enforcement,
 Proceedings, violations, **21 § 883**
Expenses and expenditures, diversion control programs, funds from Diver-
  sion Control Fee Account, reimbursement, **21 § 886a**
Exports and imports, administration and enforcement provisions, applicabili-
  ty, **21 § 965**
Felonies, arrest, **21 § 878**
Informers, rewards, payments, advances, **21 § 886**
Liabilities, civil and criminal, **21 § 885**
Payments, advances, **21 § 886**
Searches and seizures, **21 § 878**
Subpoenas, **21 § 878**
Summons, **21 § 878**
Tort claims, foreign countries, payment, **21 § 904**
Treasury Department, Attorney General to direct advance of funds, **21 § 886**
Violations, enforcement proceedings, **21 § 883**

DRUG FREE COMMUNITIES
Controlled Substances, this index

DRUG FREE MEDIA CAMPAIGN ACT OF 1998
Generally, **21 § 1801 et seq.**

DRUG LISTING ACT OF 1972
Generally, **21 §§ 301 nt, 331, 335, 360, 360 nt**

DRUG POSSESSION PENALTY ACT OF 1986
Generally, **21 § 844**

DRUGGISTS AND DRUG STORES
Pharmacists, generally, this index

906

section, inspection was limited to administrative inspection and was conducted in accordance with this section, any matters revealed by such inspection were not subject to suppression in criminal proceeding. U.S. v. Prendergast, W.D.Pa.1977, 436 F.Supp. 931, affirmed 585 F.2d 69.

Where subsequent statements made by defendant were directly related to information gathered by Drug Enforcement Agency compliance officers as result of illegal search of defendant's pharmacy, defendant was entitled to suppression of such statements. U. S. v. Enserro, W.D.N.Y.1975, 401 F.Supp. 460.

§ 881. Forfeitures

(a) Subject property

The following shall be subject to forfeiture to the United States and no property right shall exist in them:

(1) All controlled substances which have been manufactured, distributed, dispensed, or acquired in violation of this subchapter.

(2) All raw materials, products, and equipment of any kind which are used, or intended for use, in manufacturing, compounding, processing, delivering, importing, or exporting any controlled substance or listed chemical in violation of this subchapter.

(3) All property which is used, or intended for use, as a container for property described in paragraph (1), (2), or (9).

(4) All conveyances, including aircraft, vehicles, or vessels, which are used, or are intended for use, to transport, or in any manner to facilitate the transportation, sale, receipt, possession, or concealment of property described in paragraph (1), (2), or (9), except that—

(A) no conveyance used by any person as a common carrier in the transaction of business as a common carrier shall be forfeited under the provisions of this section unless it shall appear that the owner or other person in charge of such conveyance was a consenting party or privy to a violation of this subchapter or subchapter II of this chapter;

(B) no conveyance shall be forfeited under the provisions of this section by reason of any act or omission established by the owner thereof to have been committed or omitted by any person other than such owner while such conveyance was unlawfully in the possession of a person other than the owner in violation of the criminal laws of the United States, or of any State; and

(C) no conveyance shall be forfeited under this paragraph to the extent of an interest of an owner, by reason of any act or omission established by that owner to have been commit-

245

ted or omitted without the knowledge, consent, or willful blindness of the owner.

(5) All books, records, and research, including formulas, microfilm, tapes, and data which are used, or intended for use, in violation of this subchapter.

(6) All moneys, negotiable instruments, securities, or other things of value furnished or intended to be furnished by any person in exchange for a controlled substance or listed chemical in violation of this subchapter, all proceeds traceable to such an exchange, and all moneys, negotiable instruments, and securities used or intended to be used to facilitate any violation of this subchapter, except that no property shall be forfeited under this paragraph, to the extent of the interest of an owner, by reason of any act or omission established by that owner to have been committed or omitted without the knowledge or consent of that owner.

(7) All real property, including any right, title, and interest (including any leasehold interest) in the whole of any lot or tract of land and any appurtenances or improvements, which is used, or intended to be used, in any manner or part, to commit, or to facilitate the commission of, a violation of this subchapter punishable by more than one year's imprisonment, except that no property shall be forfeited under this paragraph, to the extent of an interest of an owner, by reason of any act or omission established by that owner to have been committed or omitted without the knowledge or consent of that owner.

(8) All controlled substances which have been possessed in violation of this subchapter.

(9) All listed chemicals, all drug manufacturing equipment, all tableting machines, all encapsulating machines, and all gelatin capsules, which have been imported, exported, manufactured, possessed, distributed, dispensed, acquired, or intended to be distributed, dispensed, acquired, imported, or exported, in violation of this subchapter or subchapter II of this chapter.

(10) Any drug paraphernalia (as defined in section 1822 of the Mail Order Drug Paraphernalia Control Act).

(11) Any firearm (as defined in section 921 of Title 18) used or intended to be used to facilitate the transportation, sale, receipt, possession, or concealment of property described in paragraph (1) or (2) and any proceeds traceable to such property.

(b) Seizure pursuant to Supplemental Rules for Certain Admiralty and Maritime Claims; issuance of warrant authorizing seizure

Any property subject to civil forfeiture to the United States under this subchapter may be seized by the Attorney General upon process
246

issued pursuant to the Supplemental Rules for Certain Admiralty and Maritime Claims by any district court of the United States having jurisdiction over the property, except that seizure without such process may be made when—

>   **(1)** the seizure is incident to an arrest or a search under a search warrant or an inspection under an administrative inspection warrant;

>   **(2)** the property subject to seizure has been the subject of a prior judgment in favor of the United States in a criminal injunction or forfeiture proceeding under this subchapter;

>   **(3)** the Attorney General has probable cause to believe that the property is directly or indirectly dangerous to health or safety; or

>   **(4)** the Attorney General has probable cause to believe that the property is subject to civil forfeiture under this subchapter.

In the event of seizure pursuant to paragraph (3) or (4) of this subsection, proceedings under subsection (d) of this section shall be instituted promptly.

The Government may request the issuance of a warrant authorizing the seizure of property subject to forfeiture under this section in the same manner as provided for a search warrant under the Federal Rules of Criminal Procedure.

(c) Custody of Attorney General

Property taken or detained under this section shall not be repleviable, but shall be deemed to be in the custody of the Attorney General, subject only to the orders and decrees of the court or the official having jurisdiction thereof. Whenever property is seized under any of the provisions of this subchapter, the Attorney General may—

>   **(1)** place the property under seal;

>   **(2)** remove the property to a place designated by him; or

>   **(3)** require that the General Services Administration take custody of the property and remove it, if practicable, to an appropriate location for disposition in accordance with law.

(d) Other laws and proceedings applicable

The provisions of law relating to the seizure, summary and judicial forfeiture, and condemnation of property for violation of the customs laws; the disposition of such property or the proceeds from the sale thereof; the remission or mitigation of such forfeitures; and the compromise of claims shall apply to seizures and forfeitures incurred, or alleged to have been incurred, under any of the provisions of this subchapter, insofar as applicable and not inconsistent with the provisions hereof; except that such duties as are imposed upon the

247

customs officer or any other person with respect to the seizure and forfeiture of property under the customs laws shall be performed with respect to seizures and forfeitures of property under this subchapter by such officers, agents, or other persons as may be authorized or designated for that purpose by the Attorney General, except to the extent that such duties arise from seizures and forfeitures effected by any customs officer.

(e) Disposition of forfeited property

(1) Whenever property is civilly or criminally forfeited under this subchapter the Attorney General may—

(A) retain the property for official use or, in the manner provided with respect to transfers under section 1616a of Title 19, transfer the property to any Federal agency or to any State or local law enforcement agency which participated directly in the seizure or forfeiture of the property;

(B) except as provided in paragraph (4), sell, by public sale or any other commercially feasible means, any forfeited property which is not required to be destroyed by law and which is not harmful to the public;

(C) require that the General Services Administration take custody of the property and dispose of it in accordance with law;

(D) forward it to the Drug Enforcement Administration for disposition (including delivery for medical or scientific use to any Federal or State agency under regulations of the Attorney General); or

(E) transfer the forfeited personal property or the proceeds of the sale of any forfeited personal or real property to any foreign country which participated directly or indirectly in the seizure or forfeiture of the property, if such a transfer—

(i) has been agreed to by the Secretary of State;

(ii) is authorized in an international agreement between the United States and the foreign country; and

(iii) is made to a country which, if applicable, has been certified under section 2291j(b) of Title 22.

(2)(A) The proceeds from any sale under subparagraph (B) of paragraph (1) and any moneys forfeited under this title shall be used to pay—

(i) all property expenses of the proceedings for forfeiture and sale including expenses of seizure, maintenance of custody, advertising, and court costs; and

(ii) awards of up to $100,000 to any individual who provides original information which leads to the arrest and conviction of a

248

person who kills or kidnaps a Federal drug law enforcement agent.

Any award paid for information concerning the killing or kidnapping of a Federal drug law enforcement agent, as provided in clause (ii), shall be paid at the discretion of the Attorney General.

(B) The Attorney General shall forward to the Treasurer of the United States for deposit in accordance with section 524(c) of Title 28, any amounts of such moneys and proceeds remaining after payment of the expenses provided in subparagraph (A), except that, with respect to forfeitures conducted by the Postal Service, the Postal Service shall deposit in the Postal Service Fund, under section 2003(b)(7) of Title 39, such moneys and proceeds.

(3) The Attorney General shall assure that any property transferred to a State or local law enforcement agency under paragraph (1)(A)—

(A) has a value that bears a reasonable relationship to the degree of direct participation of the State or local agency in the law enforcement effort resulting in the forfeiture, taking into account the total value of all property forfeited and the total law enforcement effort with respect to the violation of law on which the forfeiture is based; and

(B) will serve to encourage further cooperation between the recipient State or local agency and Federal law enforcement agencies.

(4)(A) With respect to real property described in subparagraph (B), if the chief executive officer of the State involved submits to the Attorney General a request for purposes of such subparagraph, the authority established in such subparagraph is in lieu of the authority established in paragraph (1)(B).

(B) In the case of property described in paragraph (1)(B) that is civilly or criminally forfeited under this subchapter, if the property is real property that is appropriate for use as a public area reserved for recreational or historic purposes or for the preservation of natural conditions, the Attorney General, upon the request of the chief executive officer of the State in which the property is located, may transfer title to the property to the State, either without charge or for a nominal charge, through a legal instrument providing that—

(i) such use will be the principal use of the property; and

(ii) title to the property reverts to the United States in the event that the property is used otherwise.

(f) Forfeiture and destruction of schedule I and II substances

(1) All controlled substances in schedule I or II that are possessed, transferred, sold, or offered for sale in violation of the provisions of

249

this subchapter; all dangerous, toxic, or hazardous raw materials or products subject to forfeiture under subsection (a)(2) of this section; and any equipment or container subject to forfeiture under subsection (a)(2) or (3) of this section which cannot be separated safely from such raw materials or products shall be deemed contraband and seized and summarily forfeited to the United States. Similarly, all substances in schedule I or II, which are seized or come into the possession of the United States, the owners of which are unknown, shall be deemed contraband and summarily forfeited to the United States.

(2) The Attorney General may direct the destruction of all controlled substances in schedule I or II seized for violation of this subchapter; all dangerous, toxic, or hazardous raw materials or products subject to forfeiture under subsection (a)(2) of this section; and any equipment or container subject to forfeiture under subsection (a)(2) or (3) of this section which cannot be separated safely from such raw materials or products under such circumstances as the Attorney General may deem necessary.

(g) Plants

(1) All species of plants from which controlled substances in schedules I and II may be derived which have been planted or cultivated in violation of this subchapter, or of which the owners or cultivators are unknown, or which are wild growths, may be seized and summarily forfeited to the United States.

(2) The failure, upon demand by the Attorney General or his duly authorized agent, of the person in occupancy or in control of land or premises upon which such species of plants are growing or being stored, to produce an appropriate registration, or proof that he is the holder thereof, shall constitute authority for the seizure and forfeiture.

(3) The Attorney General, or his duly authorized agent, shall have authority to enter upon any lands, or into any dwelling pursuant to a search warrant, to cut, harvest, carry off, or destroy such plants.

(h) Vesting of title in United States

All right, title, and interest in property described in subsection (a) of this section shall vest in the United States upon commission of the act giving rise to forfeiture under this section.

(i) Stay of civil forfeiture proceedings

The filing of an indictment or information alleging a violation of this subchapter or subchapter II of this chapter, or a violation of State or local law that could have been charged under this subchap-

250

ter or subchapter II of this chapter which is also related to a civil forfeiture proceeding under this section shall, upon motion of the United States and for good cause shown, stay the civil forfeiture proceeding.

(j) Venue

In addition to the venue provided for in section 1395 of Title 28 or any other provision of law, in the case of property of a defendant charged with a violation that is the basis for forfeiture of the property under this section, a proceeding for forfeiture under this section may be brought in the judicial district in which the defendant owning such property is found or in the judicial district in which the criminal prosecution is brought.

(*l*) [1] Agreement between Attorney General and Postal Service for performance of functions

The functions of the Attorney General under this section shall be carried out by the Postal Service pursuant to such agreement as may be entered into between the Attorney General and the Postal Service.

(Pub.L. 91–513, Title II, § 511, Oct. 27, 1970, 84 Stat. 1276; Pub.L. 95–633, Title III, § 301(a), Nov. 10, 1978, 92 Stat. 3777; Pub.L. 96–132, § 14, Nov. 30, 1979, 93 Stat. 1048; Pub.L. 98–473, Title II, §§ 306, 309, 518, Oct. 12, 1984, 98 Stat. 2050, 2051, 2075; Pub.L. 99–570, Title I, §§ 1006(c), 1865, 1992, Oct. 27, 1986, 100 Stat. 3207–7, 3207–54, 3207–60; Pub.L. 99–646, § 74, Nov. 10, 1986, 100 Stat. 3618; Pub.L. 100–690, Titles V, VI, §§ 5105, 6059, 6074, 6075, 6077(a), (b), 6253, Nov. 18, 1988, 102 Stat. 4301, 4319, 4323–4325, 4363; Pub.L. 101–189, Div. A, Title XII, § 1215(a), Nov. 29, 1989, 103 Stat. 1569; Pub.L. 101–647, Title XX, §§ 2003, 2004, 2007, 2008, Nov. 29, 1990, 104 Stat. 4855, 4856; Pub.L. 102–239, § 2, Dec. 17, 1991, 105 Stat. 1912; Pub.L. 102–583, § 6(a), Nov. 2, 1992, 106 Stat. 4932; Pub.L. 103–447, Title I, §§ 102(d), 103(a), Nov. 2, 1994, 108 Stat. 4693; Pub.L. 104–237, Title II, § 201(b), Oct. 3, 1996, 110 Stat. 3101.)

[1] So in original. No subsec. (k) has been enacted.

HISTORICAL AND STATUTORY NOTES

Revision Notes and Legislative Reports

1970 Acts. House Report No. 91–1444 and Conference Report No. 91–1603, see 1970 U.S. Code Cong. and Adm. News, p. 4566.

1978 Acts. House Report No. 95–1193, see 1978 U.S. Code Cong. and Adm. News, p. 9496.

1979 Acts. Senate Report No. 96–173 and House Conference Report No. 96–628, see 1979 U.S. Code Cong. and Adm. News, p. 2003.

1984 Acts. House Report No. 98–1030 and House Conference Report No. 98–1159, see 1984 U.S. Code Cong. and Adm. News, p. 3182.

1986 Acts. Statement by President, see 1986 U.S. Code Cong. and Adm. News, p. 5393.

House Report No. 99–797, see 1986 U.S. Code Cong. and Adm. News, p. 6138.

1988 Acts. For Related Reports, see 1988 U.S. Code Cong. and Adm. News, p. 5937.

1989 Acts. House Report No. 101–121, House Conference Report No. 101–331, and Statement by President, see 1989 U.S. Code Cong. and Adm. News, p. 838.

251

1990 Acts. House Report Nos. 101–681(Parts I and II) and 101–736, Senate Report No. 101–460, and Statement by President, see 1990 U.S. Code Cong. and Adm. News, p. 6472.

1991 Acts. House Report No. 102–359, and Statement by President, see 1991 U.S. Code Cong. and Adm. News, p. 1518.

1994 Acts. Related House Report No. 103–724, see 1994 U.S. Code Cong. and Adm. News, p. 3682.

References in Text

"This subchapter", referred to in text, was in the original "this title" which is Title II of Pub.L. 91–513, Oct. 27, 1970, 84 Stat. 1242, and is popularly known as the "Controlled Substances Act". For complete classification of Title II to the Code, see Short Title note set out under § 801 of this title and Tables.

"Subchapter II of this chapter", referred to in subsec. (a)(4)(A), was in the original "title III", meaning Title III of Pub.L. 91–513, Oct. 27, 1970, 84 Stat. 1285. Part A of Title III comprises subchapter II of this chapter. For classification of Part B, consisting of sections 1101 to 1105 of Title III, see Tables.

The criminal laws of the United States, referred to in subsec. (a)(4)(B), are classified generally to Title 18, Crimes and Criminal Procedure.

Section 1822 of the Mail Order Drug Paraphernalia Control Act, referred to in subsec. (a)(10), is section 1822 of Pub.L. 99–570, title I, Oct. 27, 1986, 100 Stat. 3207—51, which was repealed by Pub.L. 101–647, title XXIV, § 2401(d), Nov. 29, 1990, 104 Stat. 4859. Prior to repeal, subsec. (d) of section 1822 of Pub.L. 99–570, which defined "drug paraphernalia", was transferred to subsec. (d) of section 422 of title II of Pub.L. 91–513, the Controlled Substances Act. Section 422 of Pub.L. 91–513 is classified to section 863 of this title.

The Supplemental Rules for Certain Admiralty and Maritime Claims, referred to in subsec. (b), are set out in Title 28, Judiciary and Judicial Procedure.

The Federal Rules of Criminal Procedure, referred to in subsec. (b), are set out in Title 18, Crimes and Criminal procedure.

The customs laws, referred to in subsec. (d), are classified generally to Title 19, Customs Duties.

Schedules I and II, referred to in subsecs. (f) and (g)(1), are set out in § 812(c) of this title.

Codifications

"Drug Enforcement Administration" was substituted for "Bureau of Narcotics and Dangerous Drugs" in former subsec. (e)(4), now (e)(1)(D) to conform to congressional intent manifest in amendment of § 802(4) of this title by Pub.L. 96–132, § 16(a), Nov. 30, 1979, 93 Stat. 1049, now defining term "Drug Enforcement Administration" as used in this subchapter.

Amendments

1996 Amendments. Subsec. (a)(2), (6). Pub.L. 104–237, § 201(b)(1), added "or listed chemical" following "controlled substance", wherever appearing.

Subsec. (a)(9). Pub.L. 104–237, § 201(b)(2)(A), added "dispensed, acquired," following "distributed," wherever appearing.

Pub.L. 104–237, § 201(b)(2)(B), struck out "a felony provision of" following ", imported, or exported, in violation of".

1994 Amendments. Subsec. (e)(1)(E)(iii). Pub.L. 103–447, § 102(d), substituted "section 2291j(b) of Title 22" for "section 2291(h) of Title 22".

Pub.L. 103–447, § 103(a), repealed Pub.L. 102–583, § 6(a), set out in the credit. Repeal served to undo the 1992 change in text of subsec. (e)(2)(E)(iii) under Pub.L. 102–583 and return the text to subsec. (e)(2)(E)(iii) as if no change in text had ever occurred.

1992 Amendments. Subsec. (e)(1)(E)(iii). Pub.L. 102–583, § 6(a), substituted "section 2291j of Title 22" for "section 2291(h) of Title 22" and directed that, after Sept. 30, 1994, reference to section 2291j of Title 22 was to be deemed reference to section 2291k of Title 22.

1991 Amendments. Subsec. (e)(1)(B). Pub.L. 102–239, § 2(1), inserted provisions relating to par. (4).

Subsec. (e)(4). Pub.L. 102–239, § 2(2), added par. (4).

1990 Amendments. Subsec. (a)(10). Pub.L. 101–647, § 2007, added par. (10).

Subsec. (a)(11). Pub.L. 101–647, § 2008, added par. (11).

Subsec. (e)(1)(B). Pub.L. 101–647, § 2003, inserted ", by public sale or any other commercially feasible means," after "sell".

Subsec. (f). Pub.L. 101–647, § 2004, inserted "; all dangerous, toxic, or hazardous raw materials or products subject to forfeiture under subsection (a)(2) of this section; and any equipment or container subject to forfeiture under subsection (a)(2) or (3) of this section which cannot be separated safely from such raw materials or products" after "this subchapter" wherever appearing.

1989 Amendments. Subsec. (e)(3)(B). Pub.L. 101–189, § 1215(a), substituted "will serve to encourage further cooperation between the recipient State or local agency and Federal law enforcement agencies" for "is not so transferred to circumvent any requirement of State law that prohibits forfeiture or limits use or disposition of property forfeited to State or local agencies".

1988 Amendments. Subsec. (a)(3). Pub.L. 100–690, § 6059(b), inserted reference to par. (9).

Subsec. (a)(4). Pub.L. 100–690, §§ 6059(b), 6075(1)–(3), inserted in introductory text reference to par. (9); and struck out in subpar. (A) after the semicolon the word "and", substituted in subpar. (B) "; and" for the period, and added subpar. (C).

Subsec. (a)(9). Pub.L. 100–690, § 6059(a), added par. (9).

Subsec. (e)(1)(A). Pub.L. 100–690, § 6077(b), substituted "or, in the manner provided with respect to transfers under section 1616a of Title 19, transfer the property to any Federal agency or to any State or local law enforcement agency which participated directly in the seizure or forfeiture of the property" for "or transfer the custody or ownership of any forfeited property to any Federal, State, or local agency pursuant to section 1616a of Title 19".

Subsec. (e)(1)(C) to (E). Pub.L. 100–690, § 6074(1)–(3), struck in subpar. (C) after the semicolon the word "or"; substituted in subpar. (D) "; or" for the period; and added subpar. (E).

Subsec. (e)(2)(B). Pub.L. 100–690, § 6253(b), provided for deposit of moneys

and proceeds in the Postal Service Fund in cases of forfeitures conducted by the Postal Service.

Subsec. (e)(3). Pub.L. 100–690, § 6077(a), added par. (3).

Subsec. (*l*). Pub.L. 100–690, § 6253(a), added subsec. (*l*).

1986 Amendments. Subsec. (b). Pub.L. 99–570, § 1865(1), in provisions preceding par. (1), struck out "or criminal" after "Any property subject to civil".

Pub.L. 99–570, § 1865(3), added provisions, following numbered pars., that the Government may request the issuance of a warrant authorizing the seizure of property subject to forfeiture under this section in the same manner as provided for a search warrant under the Federal Rules of Criminal Procedure.

Subsec. (b)(4). Pub.L. 99–570, § 1865(2), struck out "or criminal" after "is subject to civil".

Subsec. (e). Pub.L. 99–570, § 1992, designated existing provisions in part as par. (1), in par. (1), as so designated, further redesignated former pars. (1) to (4) as subpars. (A) to (D), respectively, redesignated remaining provisions as par. (2), in par. (2) as so redesignated struck out provisions relating to authority of the Attorney General to insure equitable transfer of any forfeited property and provisions that decisions by the Attorney General pursuant to par. (1) were not to be subject to review, substituted references to property expenses for reference to proper expenses, and added provisions for payment of awards, in the discretion of the Attorney General, of up to $100,000 to any individual who provides original information leading to the arrest and conviction of a person who kills or kidnaps a Federal drug law enforcement agent.

Subsec. (f)(1). Pub.L. 99–570, § 1006(c)(2), designated existing provisions as par. (1).

Pub.L. 99–570, § 1006(c)(1), in par. (1), as so designated, inserted "or II" after "I" wherever appearing.

Subsec. (f)(2). Pub.L. 99–570, § 1006(c)(3), added par. (2).

Subsec. (i). Pub.L. 99–570, § 1865(b), inserted ", or a violation of State or local law that could have been charged under this subchapter or subchapter II of this

253

chapter," after "a violation of this subchapter or subchapter II of this chapter".

1984 Amendments. Subsec. (a)(7). Pub.L. 98–473, § 306(a), added subsec. (a)(7).

Subsec. (a)(8). Pub.L. 98–473, § 518, added subsec. (a)(8).

Subsec. (b). Pub.L. 98–473, § 306(b)(1), added "civil or criminal" following "property subject to".

Subsec. (b)(4). Pub.L. 98–473, § 306(b)(2), substituted "is subject to civil or criminal forfeiture under" for "has been used or is intended to be used in violation of".

Subsec. (c). Pub.L. 98–473, § 306(c)(1), added "any of" following "seized under".

Subsec. (c)(3). Pub.L. 98–473, § 306(c)(2), added ", if practicable," following "remove it".

Subsec. (d). Pub.L. 98–473, § 306(d), added "any of" following "incurred, under".

Subsec. (e). Pub.L. 98–473, § 306(e)(1), added "civilly or criminally" following "Whenever property is".

Pub.L. 98–473, § 309(b), added provisions relating to authority of Attorney General to insure equitable transfer of any forfeited property.

Pub.L. 98–473, § 309(c), substituted provisions relating to section 524(c) of Title 28, for provisions relating to the general fund of the United States Treasury.

Subsec. (e)(1). Pub.L. 98–473, § 309(a), added provisions relating to transfer of custody or ownership of forfeited property.

Subsec. (e)(3). Pub.L. 98–473, § 306(e)(2), struck out provisions relating to removal of property.

Subsecs. (h) to (j). Pub.L. 98–473, § 306(f), added subsecs. (h) to (j).

1979 Amendments. Subsec. (d). Pub.L. 96–132 substituted "The provisions" for "All provisions", and struck out "and the award of compensation to informers in respect of such forfeitures" following "compromise of claims".

1978 Amendments. Subsec. (a)(6). Pub.L. 95–633, § 301(1), added par. (6).

Subsec. (e). Pub.L. 95–633, § 301(a)(2), (3), struck out of cl. (2) provi-

sions relating to use of proceeds of sale and added provision relating to the forwarding by the Attorney General of money and proceeds remaining after payment of expenses.

Effective Dates

1992 Acts. Substitution in subsec. (e)(1)(iii) of "section 2291j of Title 22" for "section 2291(h) of Title 22" by Pub.L. 102–583 effective Oct. 1, 1992, see section 6(a) of Pub.L. 102–583, set out as a note under section 2291h of Title 22, Foreign Relations and Intercourse.

1989 Acts. Section 1215(b) of Pub.L. 101–189 provided that: "The amendment made by subsection (a) [amending subsec. (e)(3)(B) of this section] shall take effect as of October 1, 1989."

1988 Acts. Section 6077(c) of Pub.L. 100–690, as amended Pub.L. 101–162, Title II, § 208, Nov. 21, 1989, 103 Stat. 1005, provided that: "Section 551(e)(3)(B) [probably means 511(e)(3)(B)] of the Controlled Substances Act, as enacted by subsection (a) [subsec. (e)(3)(B) of this section], shall apply with respect to fiscal years beginning after September 30, 1991."

Amendment by section 6059 of Pub.L. 100–690 effective 120 days after Nov. 18, 1988, see section 6061 of Pub.L. 100–690, set out as a note under section 802 of this title.

1970 Acts. Section effective Oct. 27, 1970, see § 704(b) of Pub.L. 91–513, set out as a note under § 801 of this title.

Constructive Seizure Procedures

Pub.L. 101–225, Title II, § 210, Dec. 12, 1989, 103 Stat. 1913, provided that: "Not later than 6 months after the date of enactment of this Act [Dec. 12, 1989], the Secretary of Transportation and the Secretary of the Treasury, in order to avoid the devastating economic effects on innocent owners of seizures of their vessels, shall develop a procedure for constructive seizure of vessels of the United States engaged in commercial service as defined in section 2101 of title 46, United States Code [46 U.S.C.A. § 2101], that are suspected of being used for committing violations of law involving personal use quantities of controlled substances."

Regulations for Expedited Administrative Forfeiture Procedures

Section 6079 of Pub.L. 100–690 provided that:

254

"(a) In general.—Not later than 90 days after the date of enactment of this Act [Nov. 18, 1988], the Attorney General and the Secretary of the Treasury shall consult, and after providing a 30–day public comment period, shall prescribe regulations for expedited administrative procedures for seizures under section 511(a)(4), (6), and (7) of the Controlled Substances Act (21 U.S.C. 881(a)(4), (6), and (7)); section 596 of the Tariff Act of 1930 (19 U.S.C. 1595a(a)); and section 2 of the Act of August 9, 1939 (53 Stat. 1291; 49 U.S.C. App. 782) for violations involving the possession of personal use quantities of a controlled substance.

"(b) Specifications.—The regulations prescribed pursuant to subsection (a) shall—

"(1) minimize the adverse impact caused by prolonged detention, and

"(2) provide for a final administrative determination of the case within 21 days of seizure, or provide a procedure by which the defendant can obtain release of the property pending a final determination of the case. Such regulations shall provide that the appropriate agency official rendering a final determination shall immediately return the property if the following conditions are established:

"(A) the owner or interested party did not know of or consent to the violation;

"(B) the owner establishes a valid, good faith interest in the seized property as owner or otherwise; and

"(C)(1) the owner establishes that the owner at no time had any knowledge or reason to believe that the property in which the owner claims an interest was being or would be used in a violation of the law; and

"(2) if the owner at any time had, or should have had, knowledge or reason to believe that the property in which the owner claims an interest was being or would be used in a violation of the law, that the owner did what reasonably could be expected to prevent the violation.

An owner shall not have the seized property returned under this subsection if the owner had not acted in a normal and customary manner to ascertain how the property would be used.

"(c) Notice.—At the time of seizure or upon issuance of a summons to appear under subsection (d), the officer making the seizure shall furnish to any person in possession of the conveyance a written notice specifying the procedures under this section. At the earliest practicable opportunity after determining ownership of the seized conveyance, the head of the department or agency that seizes the conveyance shall furnish a written notice to the legal and factual basis of the seizure.

"(d) Summons in lieu of seizure of commercial fishing industry vessels.— Not later than 90 days after the enactment of this Act [Nov. 18, 1988], the Attorney General, the Secretary of the Treasury, and the Secretary of Transportation shall prescribe joint regulations, after a public comment period of at least 30 days, providing for issuance of a summons to appear in lieu of seizure of a commercial fishing industry vessel as defined in section 2101 (11a), (11b), and (11c) of title 46, United States Code [46 U.S.C.A. § 2101 (11a), (11b), (11c)], for violations involving the possession of personal use quantities of a controlled substance. These regulations shall apply when the violation is committed on a commercial fishing industry vessel that is proceeding to or from a fishing area or intermediate port of call, or is actively engaged in fishing operations. The authority provided under this section shall not affect existing authority to arrest an individual for drug-related offenses or to release that individual into the custody of the vessel's master. Upon answering a summons to appear, the procedures set forth in subsections (a), (b), and (c) of this section shall apply. The jurisdiction of the district court for any forfeiture incurred shall not be affected by the use of a summons under this section.

"(e) Personal use quantities of a controlled substance.—For the purposes of this section, personal use quantities of a controlled substance shall not include sweepings or other evidence of nonpersonal use amounts."

AMERICAN LAW REPORTS

Application of forfeiture provisions of Uniform Controlled Substances Act or similar statute where drugs were possessed for personal use. 1 ALR5th 375.

255

Effect of forfeiture proceedings under Uniform Controlled Substances Act or similar statute on lien against property subject to forfeiture. 1 ALR5th 317.

Forfeitability of property, under Uniform Controlled Substances Act or similar statute, where property or evidence supporting forfeiture was illegally seized. 1 ALR5th 346.

Delay in setting hearing date or in holding hearing as affecting forfeitability under Uniform Controlled Substances Act or similar statute. 6 ALR5th 711.

Forfeitability of property under Uniform Controlled Substances Act or similar statute where amount of controlled substance seized is small. 6 ALR5th 652.

Forfeitability of property held in marital estate under Uniform Controlled Substances Act or similar statute. 84 ALR4th 620.

Forfeiture of money to state or local authorities based on its association with or proximity to other contraband. 38 ALR4th 496.

Necessity of conviction of offense associated with property seized in order to support forfeiture of property to state or local authorities. 38 ALR4th 515.

Real property as subject of forfeiture under Uniform Controlled Substances Act or similar statutes. 86 ALR4th 995.

Validity and construction of provisions of Uniform Controlled Substances Act providing for forfeiture hearing before law enforcement officer. 84 ALR4th 637.

Timeliness of institution of proceedings for forfeiture under Uniform Controlled Substances Act or similar statute. 90 ALR4th 493.

Federal Government liability for loss of, or damage to, vessels or vehicles seized in course of drug enforcement activity. 93 ALR Fed 886.

Forfeiture of personal property used in illegal manufacture, processing, or sale of controlled substances under § 511 of Comprehensive Drug Abuse Prevention and Control Act of 1970 (21 USCA § 881). 59 ALR Fed 765.

Right of mortgagee and/or lienor to compensation when property subject to mortgage and/or lien is taken by federal governmental forfeiture based on criminal acts of owner. 136 ALR Fed 593

What constitutes establishment of prima facie case for forfeiture of real property traceable to proceeds from sale of controlled substances under § 511(a)(6) of Comprehensive Drug Abuse Prevention and Control Act of 1970 (21 U.S.C.A. § 881(a)(6)). 146 ALR Fed 597.

Who is exempt from forfeiture of conveyances under 'innocent owner' provision of 21 USCA § 881(a)(4). 112 ALR Fed 589.

Who is exempt from forfeiture of drug proceeds under 'innocent owner' provision of 21 USCA § 881(a)(6). 109 ALR Fed 322.

Who is exempt from forfeiture of real property under 'innocent owner ' provision of 21 USCA § 881(a)(7). 110 ALR Fed 569.

LIBRARY REFERENCES

Administrative Law

Administrative policies, practices, and procedures, see 21 CFR § 1316.01 et seq.

Inspection, search, and seizure, see 19 CFR § 162.0 et seq.

American Digest System

Drugs and Narcotics ☞190 to ☞198.

Encyclopedias

Drugs and Narcotics, see C.J.S. §§ 138 to 155.

Searches and Seizures, see C.J.S. § 220.

21A Am Jur 2d, Customs Duties and Import Regulations § 388.

25 Am Jur 2d, Drugs and Controlled Substances §§ 156, 206-210, 212, 214, 216-219, 222.

Forms

Forfeiture proceedings, see West's Federal Practice Forms § 5851 et seq.

Judgment of condemnation, forfeiture and destruction, see West's Federal Practice Forms § 4543.

256

8B Am Jur Legal Forms 2d, Forfeitures and Penalties § 123:2.

9 Federal Procedural Forms L Ed, Foods, Drugs, and Cosmetics §§ 31.421, 422, 433, 443.

Law Review and Journal Commentaries

Attention trustees: Is real property in the corpus secure from civil forfeiture under 21 U.S.C. § 881? Lois S. Woodward, 56 Ala.Law. 83 (1995).

Austin v. United States: An analysis of the application of the Eighth Amendment to civil forfeitures. 2 Geo.Mason U.L.Rev. 127 (1994).

Austin v. United States: Applicability of the eighth amendment to civil in rem forfeitures. 29 New Eng.L.Rev. 729 (1995).

Bennis v. Michigan: Contrasting views. 48 S.C.L.Rev. 357 (1997).

Bound by the sins of another: Civil forfeiture and the lack of constitutional protection for innocent owners. 76 N.C.L.Rev. 662 (1997).

"Caught in the crossfire": Protecting the innocent owner of real property from civil forfeiture under 21 U.S.C. § 881(a)(7). 65 St.John's L.Rev. 521 (1991).

Civil drug forfeitures after *James Daniel Good Real Property:* Preseizure notice and hearing do not weaken the powerful weapon in "the war on drugs". 4 Widener J.Pub.L. 663 (1995).

Civil forfeiture: A higher form of commercial law? Steven L. Schwarcz and Alan E. Rothman, 62 Fordham L.Rev. 287 (1993).

Civil forfeiture and bankruptcy: Conflicting interests of the debtor, its creditors and the government. Myron M. Sheinfeld, Teresa L. Maines and Mark W. Wege, 69 Am.Bankr.L.J. 87 (1995).

Civil forfeiture and the eight amendment after Austin. James E. Beaver, Kit G. Narodick & Joseph M. Wallin, 19 Seattle U.L.Rev. 1 (1995).

Civil forfeiture hits home: A critical analysis of *United States v. Lot 5, Fox Grove.* 79 Minn.L.Rev. 1447 (1995).

Civil forfeiture in the Second Circuit. George C. Pratt and William B. Petersen, 65 St.John's L.Rev. 653 (1991).

Civil forfeiture law: Replacing the common law with a common sense application of the excessive fines clause of the eighth amendment. Robert Lieske, 21 Wm.Mitchell L.Rev. 265 (1995).

Civil forfeiture of real property under 21 USC § 881(a)(7). Edith A. Landman and John Hieronymus, 70 Mich.B.J. 174 (1991).

Civil forfeiture under federal narcotics law: The impact of the shifting burden of proof upon the Fifth Amendment privilege against self incrimination. 14 Suffolk U.L.Rev. 679 (1990).

Civil forfeitures: Protecting the innocent owner. G. Richard Strafer, 37 U.Fla. L.Rev. 841 (1985).

Civil penalties and multiple punishment under the Double Jeopardy Clause: Some unanswered questions. David S. Rudstein, 46 Okla.L.Rev. 587 (1993).

Confusion continues in interpreting drug forfeiture statutes. 40 Vill.L.Rev. 723 (1995).

Constitutional limits on using civil remedies to achieve criminal objectives: Understanding and transcending the criminal-civil law distinction. Mary M. Cheh, 42 Hastings L.J. 1325 (1991).

Corporation's right to a jury trial under the Sixth Amendment. Alan L. Adlestein, 27 U.C.Davis L.Rev. 375 (1994).

Criminalizing civil forfeitures. Gary M. Maveal, 74 Mich.B.J. 658 (1995).

Defining excessiveness: Applying the eighth amendment to civil forfeiture after Austin v. United States. Sarah N. Welling and Medrith Lee Hager, 83 Ky.L.J. 835 (1995).

Delicate balance: Making criminal forfeiture a viable law enforcement tool and satisfying due process after United States v. James Daniel Good Real Property. 39 St. Louis L.J. 585 (1995).

Double jeopardy and SEC proceedings. John F.X. Peloso and Stuart M. Sarnoff, 212 N.Y.L.J. 3 (Oct. 20, 1994).

Double jeopardy implications of In Rem forfeiture of crime-related property: Gradual realization of a constitutional violation. Andrew L. Subin, 19 Seattle U.L.Rev. 253 (1996).

257

Double jeopardy in forfeiture law: Keeping the defense bar's winning streak alive. Richard J. Troberman, 21 J.Legis. 197 (1995).

Drug war and real estate forfeiture under 21 U.S.C. § 881: The innocent lienholder's rights. Brad A. Chapman and Kenneth W. Pearson, 21 Tex.Tech L.Rev. 2127 (1990).

Elusive Article 9 first-lien security interest: How your lien position can be eroded and how to prevent it. Lawrence F. Flick, II and Dennis Replansky, 20 UCC L.J. 211 (1988).

Excessive means: Applying the Eighth Amendment to civil in rem forfeitures under United States v. Chandler. 73 N.C.L.Rev. 2284 (1995).

Extending constitutional protection to civil forfeitures that exceed rough remedial compensation. 60 Geo.Wash.L.Rev. 194 (1991).

Fact-finding at federal sentencing: Why the guidelines should meet the rules. Deborah Young, 79 Cornell L.Rev. 299 (1994).

Federal Advisory Committee Act and the executive privilege: Resolving the separation of powers issue. 5 Seton Hall Const.L.J. 1023 (1995).

Federal civil forfeiture: An ill-conceived scheme unfairly deprives an innocent party of its property interest. Note, 62 U.Det.L.Rev. 87 (1984).

Fighting the New Crime Control Act. Kent A. Russell, 7 Cal.Law. 17 (Oct. 1987).

Final jeopardy: Merging the civil and criminal rounds in the punishment game. 46 Fla.L.Rev. 661 (1995).

Forfeiture: Procedures, interpretations, defense. Robert G. Morvillo, 210 N.Y.L.J. 3 (Aug. 3, 1993).

Forfeiture and its constitutional dimensions. Robert G. Morvillo, 209 N.Y.L.J. 3 (June 1, 1993).

Forfeiture and the Constitution. Bennett L. Gershman, 211 N.Y.L.J. 1 (Jan. 11, 1994).

Forfeiture and the Eighth Amendment. Steven L. Kessler, 210 N.Y.L.J. 1 (July 26, 1993).

Forfeiture and the innocent owner. Steven L. Kessler, 214 N.Y.L.J. 1 (Nov. 27, 1995).

Forfeiture under the Internal Revenue Code. John J. Tigue Jr., Bryan C. Skarlatos and Linda Lacewell, 210 N.Y.L.J. 3 (Aug. 31, 1993).

Forfeiture, legitimation and a due process right to counsel. William J. Genego, 59 Brook.L.Rev. 337 (1993).

From exodus to embarrassment: Civil forfeiture under the Drug Abuse Prevention and Control Act. 48 SMU L.Rev. 429 (1995).

Fugitives and forfeiture—Flouting the system or fundamental right? 83 Ky.L.J. 631 (1995).

How much is too much?: Application of the Eighth Amendment to civil forfeiture actions. Lee S. Arian, 26 U.West L.A.L.Rev. 119 (1995).

How much is too much? Civil forfeitures and the excessive fines clause after Austin v. United States. 45 Fla.L.Rev. 709 (1993).

"Innocent owner" defense in civil drug forfeitures after United States v. 92 Buena Vista Avenue: Still an uphill battle for third-party claimants. 3 Widener J.Pub.L. 995 (1994).

Innocent owner/Innocent spouse—Representing the criminal's lover. Robert E. Panoff, 66 Fla.B.J. 49 (Dec. 1992).

Innocent third parties in federal forfeiture proceedings: What are their rights? Michael F. Zeldin and Jane W. Moscowitz, 8 Crim.Just. 11 (Spring 1993).

Losing the battle, but not the war: The future use of civil forfeiture by law enforcement agencies after Austin v. United States. Note, 38 St.Louis U.L.J. 739 (1994).

Mysterious civil forfeiture laws. Robert M. Sondak, 68 Fla.B.J. 22 (March 1994).

Of forfeiture, facilitation and foreign innocent owners: Is a bank account containing parallel market funds fair game? Alan S. Fine, 16 Nova L.Rev. 1125 (1992).

Pre-hearing seizure of real property in civil forfeiture cases and the 1993 trilogy of restraint. 1994 Det.C.L.Rev. 1293.

258

Property, privacy, and the Fourth Amendment. William C. Heffernan, 60 Brook. L.Rev. 633 (1994).

Prosecutors who seize too much and the theories they love: Money laundering, facilitation, and forfeiture. 44 Duke L.J. 744.

Protecting the homestead from forfeiture. Steven L. Kessler, 212 N.Y.L.J. 1 (Sept. 14, 1994).

Real property forfeitures as a weapon in the government's war on drugs: A failure to protect innocent ownership rights. Note, 72 B.U.L.Rev. 217 (1992).

Reforming civil forfeiture law: The case for an automatic stay provision. Gary R. Brown, 67 St.John's L.Rev. 705 (1993).

Running the gauntlet: An assessment of the double jeopardy implications of criminally prosecuting drug offenders and pursuing civil forfeiture of related assets under 21 U.S.C. § 881(a)(4), (6) and (7). 70 Notre Dame L.Rev. 941 (1995).

Salvaging civil forfeiture under the Drug Abuse and Control Act. Monica P. Navarro, 41 Wayne L.Rev. 1609 (1995).

Scorched earth: How the expansion of civil forfeiture doctrine has laid waste due process. Tamara R. Piety, 45 U.Miami L.Rev. 911 (1991).

Search and seizure—Court expands scope of civil forfeiture laws. 18 Suffolk Transnat'l L.Rev. 371 (1995).

Should the ranch go free because the constable blundered? Gaining compliance with search and seizure standards in the age of asset forfeiture. William Patrick Nelson, 80 Cal.L.Rev. 1309 (1992).

So what rights does a 1972 HMET mobile home have anyway? In Austin v. United States, the Supreme Court applies the excessive fines clause to in rem civil forfeitures. 23 Cap.U.L.Rev. 797 (1994).

Some constitutional and practical considerations of civil forfeitures under 21 U.S.C. § 881. Henry C. Darmstadter and Leslie J. Mackoff, 9 Whittier L.Rev. 27 (1987).

Straw that broke the camel's back—the Supreme Court delivers a shocking blow to civil asset forfeiture sending Congress the message: "It's time for reform." 40 Loy.L.Rev. 113 (1994).

Supreme Court takes a weapon from the drug war arsenal: New defenses to civil drug forfeiture. 26 St. Mary's L.J. 157 (1994).

Symposium: Federal asset forfeiture reform. Jimmy Gurule, 21 J.Legis. 155 (1995).

Taking the ammunition away from the "war on drugs": A double jeopardy bar to 21 U.S.C. § 881 after Austin v. United States. Comment, 44 Case W.Res. L.Rev. 235 (1993).

Tax planning for criminal forfeitures. Glen A. Stankee, 33 Prac.Law. 73 (1987).

Tenancies by the entirety and federal civil forfeiture under Crime Abuse Prevention and Control Act: Clash of titans. Eric G. Zajac, 54 U.Pitt.L.Rev. 553 (1993).

The Comprehensive Crime Control Act of 1984. David Berg and Joel Androphy, 23 Hous.Law. 37 (March-April 1986).

The innocent owner defense to real property for forfeiture under the Comprehensive Crime Control Act of 1984. Note, 58 Fordham L.Rev. 471 (1989).

Tide is turning in federal forfeiture rulings. Steven L. Kessler, 209 N.Y.L.J. 1 (March 5, 1993).

Two views of Austin v. United States: Is a civil forfeiture action to collect "proceeds," pursuant to Title 21 U.S.C. section 881(A)(6) still exempt from the protections of the double jeopardy clause? Thomas W. Robertson, 23 American Journal of Criminal Law 431 (1996).

Will the Supreme Court restrain forfeiture? Jed S. Rakoff, 210 N.Y.L.J. 3 (July 8, 1993).

Federal Rules Decisions Commentaries

Parallel civil and criminal proceedings. Milton Pollack, 129 FRD 201 (1989).

259

Texts and Treatises

Bonds, Civil Fines, and Forfeitures, 5A Fed Proc L Ed §§ 10:110, 111, 123.
Criminal Procedure, 8 Fed Proc L Ed § 22:221.
Food, Drugs, and Cosmetics, 13 Fed Proc L Ed §§ 35:610-612, 35:626, 35:628-629, 35:632-649, 35:651, 35:662.

WESTLAW ELECTRONIC RESEARCH

Drugs and Narcotics cases: 138k[add key number].
See WESTLAW guide following the Explanation pages of this volume.

Notes of Decisions

Absolute immunity 153
Acquittal or dismissal of criminal charges 44
Administrative forfeiture 139
Admissibility of evidence 178
Adoption of seizure 80
Affirmative defense, innocent owners 103
Aggregation of facts, probable cause 46
Assignees, standing to challenge forfeiture 121
Assignment prohibition, defenses 94
Attorney fees 152
Attorneys, innocent owners 104
Attorneys, standing to challenge forfeiture 122
Authority of enforcement agents 91
Bank accounts, money 25
Bankruptcy trustee, standing to challenge forfeiture 123
Beneficial ownership, standing to challenge forfeiture 124
Burden of proof
　Generally 170
　Claimant 171
　Connection with offense 172
　Due process 173
　Innocent owners 105
　Probable cause 174
　Shifting of burden 175
　Standing to challenge forfeiture 125
Children, standing to challenge forfeiture 126
Circumstantial evidence, probable cause 47
Civil nature of proceedings 70
Claimant, burden of proof 171
Collateral 37
Common carriers, innocent owners 106
Common carriers, conveyances 17
Compensation 150
Complaint 159
Completed transactions 40
Concealing property 35
Connection with offense, burden of proof 172

Connection with offense, conveyances 18
Connection with offense, probable cause 48
Connection with offense, real property 28
Constitutionality 1-4
　Generally 1
　Due process 2
　Eighth amendment 3
　Ex post facto 4
Construction 5
Construction with other laws 6
Constructive trust, defenses 98
Containers 15
Continuances 88
Contraband 14
Conveyances 16-23
　Generally 16
　Common carriers 17
　Connection with offense 18
　Facilitation 19
　Mobile homes 20
　Motor vehicles 21
　Ownership 22
　Willful blindness 23
Conviction as prerequisite to forfeiture 11
Corporations, innocent owners 107
Costs 142
Court order for transfer of property 92
Creditors, standing to challenge forfeiture 127
Criminal violation 42
Criminal violation, probable cause 49
Custody of Attorney General 90
Default judgment 165
Defenses 93-101
　Generally 93
　Assignment prohibition 94
　Constructive trust 98
　Double jeopardy 95
　Laches 96
　Lack of consent 101
　Living on premises 99
　Mortgages 100
　Warrantless seizure 97
Delay in institution of proceedings 75

260

261

_____

1. Constitutionality—Generally

If seizure of property is otherwise proper, no violation of Fourth Amendment occurs when district court clerk issues warrant of arrest in rem in forfeiture action; "arrest warrant" is necessitated only by the legal fiction of an in rem action and is not a "warrant" within meaning of Fourth Amendment such that issuing authority must first make probable cause determination. U.S. v. Turner, C.A.4 (Va.) 1991, 933 F.2d 240.

Narcotics defendant's attorneys did not have standing to bring Sixth Amendment challenge to civil forfeiture of property jointly held by husband and wife that constituted proceeds of narcotics trafficking; believing that mortgages they had taken in defendant's property were entitled to priority over Government's forfeiture interest in property, attorneys conducted defendant's defense and prosecuted his appeal, and thus defendant was never denied right to counsel of his choice and there existed no Sixth Amendment violation that could support attorneys' assertion of claim to property. U.S. v. Four Parcels of Real Property on Lake Forrest Circle In Riverchase, Shelby County, Ala., C.A.11 (Ala.) 1989, 870 F.2d 586.

Provision of this section for a warrantless seizure when the Attorney General has probable cause to believe that the property has been or is intended to be used in violation of the subchapter does not require exigent circumstances, and the application of that provision does not violate U.S.C.A. Const. Amend. 4. U. S. v. One 1977 Lincoln Mark V Coupe, C.A.3 (Pa.) 1981, 643 F.2d 154, certiorari denied 102 S.Ct. 97, 454 U.S. 818, 70 L.Ed.2d 88.

Civil forfeiture of drug proceeds is a remedial sanction that does not constitute punishment for double jeopardy purposes. U.S. v. One 1989, 23 Foot, Wellcraft Motor Vessel, Puerto Rico Registration Number PR 2855GG, D.Puerto Rico 1995, 910 F.Supp. 46, affirmed 125 F.3d 842, certiorari denied 119 S.Ct. 79, 142 L.Ed.2d 62.

Conduct of trial court in drug forfeiture action involving public housing apartment was more than sufficient to protect claimant's Fifth Amendment rights; trial court allowed filing of sealed affidavits which could be withdrawn by affiants if at some later time court decided to unseal them, at no time could affidavits be used in any criminal proceedings against affiants, and while court initially ruled that stay of forfeiture proceeding was not warranted, it later stayed any forfeiture actions until pending criminal prosecutions against claimants were completed. U.S. v. Leasehold Interest in 121 Nostrand Ave., Apartment 1–C, Brooklyn, N.Y., E.D.N.Y.1991, 760 F.Supp. 1015.

Forfeiture of approximately $70,000 interest in condominium allegedly used to facilitate two cocaine sales was civil penalty which offended neither due process nor Eighth Amendment; aim of compensating Government for its efforts to prevent or mitigate harms caused by property's unlawful use was remedial goal. U.S. v. Certain Real Property and Premises Known as 38 Whalers Cove Drive, Babylon, N.Y., E.D.N.Y.1990, 747 F.Supp. 173, affirmed 954 F.2d 29, certiorari denied 113 S.Ct. 55, 506 U.S. 815, 121 L.Ed.2d 24.

A statute allowing the civil forfeiture of real property used to facilitate a narcotics transaction was not unconstitutionally vague or ambiguous as applied to a claimant who had conducted numerous cocaine sales on the property and had offered the deed to the entire property as security for future contemplated drug transaction. U.S. v. 26.075 Acres, More or Less Located in Swift Creek Tp., Wake County, N.C., E.D.N.C.1988, 687 F.Supp. 1005, affirmed in part, reversed in part 866 F.2d 1538.

Federal drug forfeiture statute's procedure for seizure of property without determination of probable cause by qualified judicial officer violates warrants clause of Fourth Amendment; at minimum, United States Attorney must secure an in rem warrant from magistrate or district court judge who has made probable cause determination. U.S. v. Life Ins. Co. of Virginia Single Premium Whole Life Policy, Policy No. 002138373, W.D.N.C.1986, 647 F.Supp. 732.

Forfeiture provision of Controlled Substances Act is not unconstitutional on ground that it permits criminal punishment by civil burden of proof in violation of the Fifth and Sixth Amendments; Congress has clearly indicated that the statute is a "civil in rem" proceeding rather than a "criminal" sanction, and purpose or effect of the statute is not so punitive that it negates congressional intent to enact a civil penalty. U.S. v. Premises Known as 2639 Meetinghouse Rd., Jamison, Pa., E.D.Pa.1986, 633 F.Supp. 979.

Forfeiture provision [21 U.S.C.A. § 881(b)] of narcotics law violates warrants clause of Fourth Amendment by authorizing issuance of in rem arrest warrant by clerk of court solely on basis of filing of verified complaint by Attorney General without determination by qualified judicial officer of whether there is probable cause for belief that connection exists between property to be seized for forfeiture and criminal activity under narcotics laws. U.S. v. One Hundred Twenty-Eight Thousand Thirty-Five Dollars (128,035.00) in U.S. Currency, S.D.Ohio 1986, 628 F.Supp. 668, appeal dismissed 806 F.2d 262.

2. —— Due process, constitutionality

Federal and Oklahoma state administrative forfeiture laws satisfy requirements of due process; both give notice to possible claimants and provide procedure by which claimants may contest pending forfeiture. U.S. v. Deninno, C.A.10 (Okla.) 1996, 103 F.3d 82.

Statute allowing seizure of property subject to forfeiture without notice and opportunity to be heard was unconstitutional as applied to seizure of house; house's owner had substantial and unique interest in house as it was his home, and government's interest in avoiding preseizure hearing was not significant since house could not be moved to another jurisdiction to avoid forfeiture. U.S. v. James Daniel Good Property Titled in Name of James Daniel Good, C.A.9 (Hawai'i) 1992, 971 F.2d 1376, amended on denial of rehearing, certiorari granted 113 S.Ct. 1576, 507 U.S. 983, 123 L.Ed.2d 145, affirmed in part, reversed in part 114 S.Ct. 492, 510 U.S. 43, 126 L.Ed.2d 490.

Seizure by Drug Enforcement Administration of home prior to institution of civil forfeiture action against owner violated due process. (Per Torruella, Circuit Judge, with whom Coffin, Circuit Judge, concurred.) Application of Kingsley, C.A.1 (Mass.) 1986, 802 F.2d 571.

In view of protections provided in sections 1602–04 of Title 19, owner of vehicle seized on the ground that it had been used to facilitate sale of controlled substance was not entitled under due process clause of U.S.C.A. Const. Amend. 5 to additional probable cause hearing within 72 hours of government's seizure of his automobile. U.S. v. One 1971 BMW 4-Door Sedan, Model 2800, Gray in Color VIN 2320587, AZ. LIC. RNM-898, C.A.9 (Ariz.) 1981, 652 F.2d 817.

Civil forfeiture statute is constitutional, despite contention that it is, in effect, a criminal forfeiture proceeding and denies due process. U.S. v. Real Property Located at 11205 McPherson Lane Ojai, Cal., D.Nev.1991, 754 F.Supp. 1483, af-

firmed 32 F.3d 573, certiorari dismissed 115 S.Ct. 536, 130 L.Ed.2d 438.

Due process was violated by government's no-notice removal of tenants in public housing pursuant to National Public Housing Asset Forfeiture Project, authorizing government to seize homes of public housing tenants without prior notice and opportunity to be heard if any leasehold resident was suspected of drug-related activity; ex parte probable cause hearings administered prior to seizure of public leaseholds did not sufficiently protect tenants' expectations of freedom and privacy in their homes. Richmond Tenants Organization, Inc. v. Kemp, E.D.Va. 1990, 753 F.Supp. 607, affirmed 956 F.2d 1300.

Seizure of real property which had been used to facilitate a narcotics transaction, without prior hearing by the United States upon a court order after ex parte review of a verified complaint and affidavit of probable cause did not deny the forfeiture claimant of her procedural due process rights. U.S. v. 26.075 Acres, More or Less Located in Swift Creek Tp., Wake County, N.C., E.D.N.C.1988, 687 F.Supp. 1005, affirmed in part, reversed in part 866 F.2d 1538.

Forfeiture statute providing for shifting burden of proof and requiring claimant to prove by preponderance of evidence that either criminal activities involving property did not occur or that claimant had no knowledge of criminal activities, after Government demonstrated probable cause to believe that there was substantial connection between property to be forfeited and criminal activity, provided appropriate procedural mechanism which comported with due process. U.S. v. Two Tracts of Real Property, Containing 30.80 Acres, More or Less, With Appurtenances, Located in Bruce Tp., Guilford County, N.C., M.D.N.C.1987, 665 F.Supp. 422, affirmed 856 F.2d 675; U.S. v. Santoro, C.A.4 (N.C.) 1989, 866 F.2d 1538.

Eventual forfeiture of money paid to attorneys which has been determined to be derived from drug crimes does not deprive attorneys of their property without due process and does not constitute unwarranted government interference with attorneys' practice of law. U.S. v. One Parcel of Land ... Commonly Known as 4204 Cedarwood, Matteson, Il, N.D.Ill.1985, 614 F.Supp. 183.

264

LEGISLATIVE HISTORY
HOUSE REPORT NO. 103-111

OMNIBUS BUDGET RECONCILIATION ACT OF 1993

P.L. 103-66, see page 107 Stat. 312

DATES OF CONSIDERATION AND PASSAGE

House: May 27, August 5, 1993

Senate: June 23, 24, 25, August 6, 1993

Cong. Record Vol. 139 (1993)

House Report (Budget Committee) No. 103-111, May 25, 1993
[To accompany H.R. 2264]

House Conference Report No. 103-213, Aug. 3, 1993
[To accompany H.R. 2264]

No Senate Report was submitted with this legislation. The House Report is set out below and the House Conference Report follows.

HOUSE REPORT NO. 103-111

[page iii]

CONTENTS

U.S.C.C.A.N.

U.S. Code Congressional & Administrative News is frequently used to update research done in U.S.C.A. For example, you can find if there has been a recent change in the law affecting the federal statute you are researching. It also has the full text to newly enacted laws, congressional and administrative highlights and various cross-referencing tables. (This section is for illustration only.)

No. 11 January 2001

UNITED STATES CODE CONGRESSIONAL AND ADMINISTRATIVE NEWS

106th Congress—Second Session

Members and Committees
Public Laws 106–358 to 106–365
Legislative History
Proclamations
Executive Orders
President's Messages
Federal Regulations
Court Rules
Tables
Index

West Group
610 Opperman Drive
Eagan, MN 55123

SESSION HIGHLIGHTS

Washington, D.C.
January, 2001

NEW LAWS

Amendments—Eligible Rollover Distributions

★ ★ ★ Pub. L. 106–361 amends title 5, United States Code, to allow for the contribution of certain rollover distributions to accounts in the Thrift Savings Plan, to eliminate certain waiting-period requirements for participating in the Thrift Savings Plan.

—Revised Organic Act

★ ★ ★ Pub. L. 106–364 amends the Revised Organic Act of the Virgin Islands to provide that the number of members on the legislature of the Virgin Islands and the number of such members constituting a quorum shall be determined by the laws of the Virgin Islands.

Coastal Barrier Resources System—Technical Corrections

★ ★ ★ Pub. L. 106–360 directs the Secretary of the Interior to make technical corrections to a map relating to the Coastal Barrier Resources System.

Continuing Appropriations

★ ★ ★ Pub. L. 106–358 and 106–359 make further continuing appropriations for the fiscal year 2001.

Defense Production Act

★ ★ ★ Pub. L. 106–363 extends and reauthorize the Defense Production Act of 1950.

Land Conveyance—Ivanpah Valley

★ ★ ★ Pub. L. 106–362 provides for the conveyance of certain Federal public lands in the Ivanpah Valley, Nevada, to Clark County, Nevada, for the development of an airport facility.

Placement of Plaque at Lincoln Memorial

★ ★ ★ Pub. L. 106–365 provides for the placement at the Lincoln Memorial of a plaque commemorating the speech of Martin Luther King, Jr., known as the "I Have A Dream" speech.

FIFTY–TWO WEEK TREASURY BILLS——————

Interest on Money Judgments

★ ★ ★ Interest on money judgments in a civil case recovered in a district court is calculated from the date of entry of the judgment at a rate equal to the equivalent coupon issue yield of the average auction price for the last auction of the fifty–two week United States Treasury bills settled immediately prior to the date of the judgment. 28 U.S.C.A §1961(a). For interest rates beginning in 1999, see table below.

Date of Auction	Equivalent Coupon Issue Yield
July 20, 1999	4.966%
August 17, 1999	5.224%
September 14, 1999	5.285%
October 13, 1999	5.411%
November 9, 1999	5.471%
December 7, 1999	5.670%

ii

January 4, 2000	5.997%
February 1, 2000	6.287%
February 29, 2000	6.197%
May 31, 2000	6.375%
August 29, 2000	6.241%
November 28, 2000	6.052%

Note:

Interest on money judgments will be updated four times a year starting February, 2000.

PRESIDENT'S MESSAGES————————————

Poor Nation Debt–Relief Funding Legislation

★ ★ ★ On November 6, 2000, President Clinton delivered a statement on remarks of "Poor Nation Debt–Relief Funding Legislation", which would provide funding for the entire $435 million needed for the United States to do its share in debt relief this year for the world's poorest countries and give the International Monetary Fund the authority it needs to do its share.

*

iii

CONTENTS

*Materials in this pamphlet are listed on Pages V and VI.

III

CONTENTS

The Congress
Laws of the 106th Congress
Second Session

*

COASTAL BARRIER RESOURCES SYSTEM—TECHNICAL CORRECTIONS

An Act To direct the Secretary of the Interior to make technical corrections to a map relating to the Coastal Barrier Resources System.

Be it enacted by the Senate and House of Representatives of the United States of America in Congress assembled,

SECTION 1.   CORRECTIONS TO MAPS.

(a) IN GENERAL.—The Secretary of the Interior shall, before the end of the 30–day period beginning on the date of the enactment of this Act, make such corrections to the map described in subsection (b) as are necessary to ensure that depictions of areas on that map are consistent with the depictions of areas appearing on the map entitled "Amendments to the Coastal Barrier Resources System", dated June 5, 2000.

(b) MAP DESCRIBED.—The map described in this subsection is the map that—

(1) is included in a set of maps entitled "Coastal Barrier Resources System", dated November 2, 1994; and

(2) relates to unit P19–P of the Coastal Barrier Resources System.

(c) AVAILABILITY.—The Secretary of the Interior shall keep the map described in subsection (b) on file and available for public inspection in accordance with section 4(b) of the Coastal Barrier Resources Act (16 U.S.C. 3503(b)).

Approved October 27, 2000.

No. 2

April, 2001

UNITED STATES CODE CONGRESSIONAL AND ADMINISTRATIVE NEWS

107th Congress—First Session

Members and Committees
Public Law 107–1
Proclamations
Executive Orders
President's Messages
Federal Regulations
Court Rules
Tables
Index

West Group
610 Opperman Drive
Eagan, MN 55123

CONTENTS

* Materials in this pamphlet are listed on Pages V and VI.

III

The Congress

Laws of the 107th Congress
First Session

*

115 Stat. 1

PUBLIC LAW 107–1 [H.J. Res. 7]; February 15, 2001

RECOGNIZING THE 90TH BIRTHDAY OF RONALD REAGAN

Joint Resolution Recognizing the 90th birthday of Ronald Reagan.

Whereas February 6, 2001, is the 90th birthday of Ronald Wilson Reagan;

Whereas both Ronald Reagan and his wife Nancy Reagan have distinguished records of public service to the United States, the American people, and the international community;

Whereas Ronald Reagan was twice elected by overwhelming margins as President of the United States;

Whereas Ronald Reagan fulfilled his pledge to help restore "the great, confident roar of American progress, growth, and optimism" and ensure renewed economic prosperity;

Whereas Ronald Reagan's leadership was instrumental in extending freedom and democracy around the globe and uniting a world divided by the Cold War;

Whereas Ronald Reagan is loved and admired by millions of Americans, and by countless others around the world;

Whereas Ronald Reagan's eloquence united Americans in times of triumph and tragedy;

Whereas Nancy Reagan not only served as a gracious First Lady but also led a national crusade against illegal drug use;

Whereas together Ronald and Nancy Reagan dedicated their lives to promoting national pride and to bettering the quality of life in the United States and throughout the world; and

Whereas the thoughts and prayers of the Congress and the country are with Ronald Reagan in his courageous battle with Alzheimer's disease: Now, therefore, be it

Resolved by the Senate and House of Representatives of the United States of America in Congress assembled, That the Congress, on behalf of the American people, extends its birthday greetings and best wishes to Ronald Reagan on his 90th birthday.

Approved February 15, 2001.

5. Special Types of Research

Legal Definitions

Occasionally, the answer to your problem depends on the legal meaning of a word or phrase. In this section, you will be introduced to three different tools for this type of research: The Popular Name Table, Black's Law Dictionary, and Words and Phrases.

Special Types of Research

Popular Name Table

If you know only the popular name of a federal law, you can find it's corresponding U.S. Code title number and section number in the U.S.C.A. Popular Name Table.

Problem

You know the name of a federal law is "Contraband Seizure Act." Find the U.S. Code title and section number under which it is classified.

UNITED STATES CODE ANNOTATED

2000
GENERAL INDEX
V to Z

Popular Name Table

POPULAR NAME TABLE
FOR
ACTS OF CONGRESS
Through Pub.L. 106–170

Generally, the initial entry under the name of an Act in this Table is the citation for the Act of Congress or Public Law which enacted the Act. The subsequent entries under each Act are the citations for Public Laws which amended the Act.

Parentheticals. The references within the parentheses following Public Law citations indicate the classifications of that Public Law to the United States Code by Code title and section. In some instances, Code classifications may not be indicated for Acts of Congress that have been repealed, superseded, obsolete, or not classified to the Code.

Notes. A reference in parentheses to a "note" indicates material set out below the text of a section in the Code. A reference in parentheses in the initial entry under an Act just to a note generally indicates an Act that was codified as a whole as a note under the referenced section of the Code.

Tables. A reference in parentheses to the Tables following the citation of a Public Law means Table II—Revised Statutes 1878 and Table III—Statutes at Large. These tables contain a chronological listing of Public Laws that have been classified to the Code together with their Code classifications and current status.

"See". The word "See" set out in parentheses preceding the Code title and section indicates that the Public Law has been repealed (in whole or in part) and that certain provisions thereof have been restated in the Code title and section specified, generally a Code title that was revised when enacted into positive law. The name of an Act preceded by the word "See" indicates an alternate name for the Act and the location within the Table for the list of Public Law citations for that Act.

"See, also,". The name of an Act preceded by the words "See, also," indicates either an Act related to the named Act or another Popular Name Act contained entirely within the named Act.

AA
  See Agricultural Act of 1970

AAA
  See Agricultural Adjustment Act of 1938

AAA Farm Relief and Inflation Act (Wagner-Lewis $500,000,000 Emergency Relief Act)
  May 12, 1933, ch. 25, 48 Stat. 31 (7 §§ 601 to 604, 607, 608, 608a to 608e, 608e–1, 609 to 620, 623, 624; 12 §§ 347, 462b, 636, 723, 771, 781, 810, 823 note, 992, 993, 1016 to 1019; See 31 §§ 5301, 5304)

AAIA
  See Airport and Airway Improvement Act of 1982

AAPA
  See Antarctic Protection Act of 1990

Abacá Production Act of 1950
  Aug. 10, 1950, ch. 673, 64 Stat. 435 (50 §§ 541 to 546)

Abandoned Barge Act of 1992
  Pub.L. 102–587, Title V, Subtitle C, Nov. 4, 1992, 106 Stat. 5081 (46 §§ 4701 to 4705)

Abandoned Infants Assistance Act of 1988
  Pub.L. 100–505, Oct. 18, 1988, 102 Stat. 2523 (42 § 670 note)
  Pub.L. 102–236, §§ 2 to 8, Dec. 12, 1991, 105 Stat. 1812 to 1816 (42 § 670 note)
  Pub.L. 104–235, Title II, Subtitle C, §§ 221, 222, Oct. 3, 1996, 110 Stat. 3091, 3092 (42 § 670 notes)

423

Consumer Education Act of 1978
Pub.L. 89–10, Apr. 11, 1965, Title III, Pt. E, as added Pub.L. 95–561, Title III, § 301(a), Nov. 1, 1978, 92 Stat. 2214 (20 §§ 2981 to 2986)

Consumer Goods Pricing Act of 1975
Pub.L. 94–145, Dec. 12, 1975, 89 Stat. 801 (15 §§ 1, 45)

Consumer Home Mortgage Assistance Act of 1974
Pub.L. 93–383, Title VII, Aug. 22, 1974, 88 Stat. 714 (12 §§ 371, 1464, 1757, 1759, 1761b, 1761d, 1763, 1772, 1782, 1786, 1788)

Consumer Leasing Act of 1976 (CLA)
Pub.L. 94–240, Mar. 23, 1976, 90 Stat. 257 (15 §§ 1601, 1640, 1667 to 1667e)

Consumer-Patient Radiation Health and Safety Act of 1981
Pub.L. 97–35, Title IX, Subtitle I, Aug. 13, 1981, 95 Stat. 598 (42 §§ 10001 to 10008)
Pub.L. 102–54, § 13(q)(13), June 13, 1991, 105 Stat. 281 (42 §§ 1004, 1007, 1008)
Pub.L. 104–66, Title I, Subtitle F, § 1061(b), Dec. 21, 1995, 109 Stat. 719 (42 § 1006)

Consumer Product Safety Act (CPSA)
Pub.L. 92–573, Oct. 27, 1972, 86 Stat. 1207 (5 §§ 5314, 5315; 15 §§ 2051 to 2084)
Pub.L. 94–273, § 31, Apr. 21, 1976, 90 Stat. 380 (15 § 2076)
Pub.L. 94–284, §§ 2, 3(b), (d), (f), 4 to 16, 17(d), May 11, 1976, 90 Stat. 503 to 510, 514 (15 §§ 2052, 2053, 2056, 2058, 2059, 2060, 2064, 2068, 2069, 2071, 2072, 2073, 2075, 2076, 2079, 2081)
Pub.L. 95–319, § 3, July 11, 1978, 92 Stat. 386 (15 §§ 2068, 2082)
Pub.L. 95–631, §§ 1 to 6, 11, Nov. 10, 1978, 92 Stat. 3742 to 3745, 3748 (15 §§ 2053, 2056, 2058, 2067, 2068, 2069, 2076, 2081)
Pub.L. 96–373, Oct. 3, 1980, 94 Stat. 1366 (15 § 2053)
Pub.L. 96–486, § 3, Dec. 1, 1980, 94 Stat. 2369 (15 § 2072)
Pub.L. 97–35, Title XII, §§ 1202, 1203(a), (c), 1204, 1205(a), 1206, 1207(a), (b), 1208 to 1210, 1211(a) to (d), (h), 1213 to 1215, Aug. 13, 1981, 95 Stat. 703, 704, 713, 716, 718, 720, 721, 723, 724 (15 §§ 2052, 2054 to 2062, 2064, 2069, 2072, 2073, 2076, 2077, 2081, 2083)
Pub.L. 97–414, § 9(j), Jan. 4, 1983, 96 Stat. 2064 (15 §§ 2055, 2060, 2064, 2068, 2080)
Pub.L. 100–418, Title I, § 1214(d), Aug. 23, 1988, 102 Stat. 1156 (15 §§ 2064, 2066)
Pub.L. 101–608, Title I, §§ 102 to 105(a), 106, 107(a), 108(a), 109, 110(a), 111(a), 112(a) to (e), 113, 114, 115(a), 116, 117, Nov. 16, 1990, 104 Stat. 3110 to 3118, 3121 (15 §§ 2053, 2055, 2056, 2058, 2061, 2064, 2066, 2068, 2069, 2077, 2081, 2084)
Pub.L. 103–437, § 5(c), Nov. 2, 1994, 108 Stat. 4582 (15 §§ 2081, 2082)

Consumer Product Safety Amendments of 1981
Pub.L. 97–35, Title XII, Subtitle A, Aug. 13, 1981, 95 Stat. 703 (7 § 135; 12 § 24; 15 §§ 1193, 1201, 1204, 1262, 1263, 1274, 1276, 1471 note, 1475, 1476, 2051 note, 2052, 2054, 2055, 2056, 2057, 2058, 2059, 2060, 2061, 2062, 2064, 2069, 2072, 2073, 2076, 2077, 2080, 2081, 2083; 21 §§ 343, 352, 353, 362)

Consumer Product Safety Commission Improvements Act of 1976
Pub.L. 94–284, May 11, 1976, 90 Stat. 503 (15 §§ 1193, 1203, 1204, 1261, 1471, 1476, 2051 note, 2052, 2053, 2056, 2058, 2059, 2060, 2064, 2068, 2069, 2071, 2072, 2073, 2075, 2076, 2078, 2079, 2080 note, 2081)

Consumer Product Safety Improvement Act of 1990
Pub.L. 101–608, Nov. 16, 1990, 104 Stat. 3110 (15 §§ 1193, 1194, 1262, 1264, 1274, 2053, 2053 note, 2054 note, 2055, 2056, 2056 note, 2058, 2058 note, 2061, 2064, 2066, 2068, 2069, 2076 note, 2076a, 2077, 2081, 2084, 2084 note)

Consumer Reporting Employment Clarification Act of 1998
Pub.L. 105–347, Nov. 2, 1998, 112 Stat. 3208 (15 §§ 1601 note, 1681a to 1681c, 1681i, 1681g, 1681k, 1681s)

Continental Scientific Drilling and Exploration Act
Pub.L. 100–441, Sept. 22, 1988, 102 Stat. 1760 (43 § 31 note)

Continuing Drug Enterprises Act of 1986
Pub.L. 99–570, Title I, Subtitle F, Oct. 27, 1986, 100 Stat. 3207–14 (21 §§ 801 note, 848)

Contraband Seizure Act
Aug. 9, 1939, ch. 618, 53 Stat. 1291 (49 §§ 781 to 788)
Aug. 1, 1956, ch. 852, § 22, 70 Stat. 911 (49 § 789)

Black's Law Dictionary

Black's Law Dictionary is the legal profession's premier legal reference work. Completely revised in 1999, Black's gives definitions for over 24,000 legal terms, and is a useful tool for anyone doing legal research.

Problem

What is the doctrine of "res ipsa loquitur"?

Black's Law Dictionary®

Seventh Edition

Bryan A. Garner
Editor in Chief

WEST GROUP

ST. PAUL, MINN., 1999

residency. 1. A place of residence, esp. an official one <the diplomat's residency>. **2.** The fact or condition of living in a given place <one year's residency to be eligible for in-state tuition>.

resident, *n.* A person who has a residence in a particular place. ● A resident is not necessarily either a citizen or a domiciliary. Cf. CITIZEN; DOMICILIARY.

resident agent. See *registered agent* under AGENT.

resident alien. See ALIEN.

residential cluster. *Land-use planning.* An area of land developed as a unit with group housing and open common space. Cf. PLANNED-UNIT DEVELOPMENT.

residential community treatment center. See HALFWAY HOUSE.

residua (ri-**zij**-oo-ə). *pl.* RESIDUUM.

residual, *adj.* Of, relating to, or constituting a residue; remaining; leftover <a residual claim> <a residual functional disability>.

residual, *n.* **1.** A leftover quantity; a remainder. **2.** (*often pl.*) A disability remaining after an illness, injury, or operation. **3.** (*usu. pl.*) A fee paid to a composer or performer for each repeated broadcast (esp. on television) of a film, program, or commercial.

residual estate. See *residuary estate* under ESTATE.

residual value. See *salvage value* under VALUE.

residuary (ri-**zij**-oo-er-ee), *adj.* Of, relating to, or constituting a residue; residual <a residuary gift>.

residuary, *n. Wills & estates.* **1.** See *residuary estate* under ESTATE. **2.** See *residuary legatee* under LEGATEE.

residuary bequest. See BEQUEST.

residuary clause. *Wills & estates.* A testamentary clause that disposes of any estate property remaining after the satisfaction of specific bequests and devises.

residuary devise. See DEVISE.

residuary devisee. See DEVISEE.

residuary estate. See ESTATE.

residuary legacy. See LEGACY.

residuary legatee. See LEGATEE.

residue. 1. Something that is left over after a part is removed or disposed of; a remainder. **2.** See *residuary estate* under ESTATE.

residuum (ri-**zij**-oo-əm). **1.** That which remains; a residue. **2.** See *residuary estate* under ESTATE. Pl. **residua** (ri-**zij**-oo-ə).

residuum rule. *Administrative law.* The principle that an agency decision based partly on hearsay evidence will be upheld on judicial review only if the decision is founded on at least some competent evidence. ● The residuum rule has generally been rejected by federal and state courts.

resignation, *n.* **1.** The act or an instance of surrendering or relinquishing an office, right, or claim. **2.** A formal notification of relinquishing an office or position. — **resign,** *vb.*

res immobiles (rays i-**moh**-bə-leez). [Latin] *Civil law.* Immovable things; chattels real. See IMMOBILIA.

res incorporales (rays in-kor-pə-**ray**-leez). [Latin] *Civil law.* Incorporeal things; intangible things that are not perceptible to the senses. See *incorporeal thing* under THING.

res integra (rays **in**-tə-grə *also* in-**teg**-rə). [Latin "an entire thing"] See RES NOVA.

res inter alios acta (rays **in**-tər **ay**-lee-ohs **ak**-tə). [Latin "a thing done between others"] **1.** *Contracts.* The common-law doctrine holding that a contract cannot unfavorably affect the rights of a person who is not a party to the contract. **2.** *Evidence.* The rule prohibiting the admission of collateral facts into evidence.

res ipsa loquitur (rays **ip**-sə **loh**-kwə-tər). [Latin "the thing speaks for itself"] **1.** *Torts.* The doctrine providing that, in some circumstances, the mere fact of an accident's occurrence raises an inference of negligence so as to establish a prima facie case. — Often shortened to *res ipsa.* — Also termed *resipsy.*

"The phrase 'res ipsa loquitur' is a symbol for the rule that the fact of the occurrence of an injury, taken with the surrounding circumstances, may permit an inference or raise a presumption of negligence, or make out a plaintiff's prima facie case, and present a question of fact for defendant to meet with an explanation. It is merely a short way of saying that the circumstances attendant on the accident are of such a nature as to justify a jury, in light of common sense and past experience, in inferring that the accident was probably the result of the defendant's negligence, in the absence of explanation or other evidence which the jury believes." Stuart M. Speiser, *The Negligence Case: Res Ipsa Loquitur* § 1:2, at 5–6 (1972).

"It is said that *res ipsa loquitur* does not apply if the cause of the harm is known. This is a dark saying. The application of the principle nearly always presupposes that some part of the causal process is known, but what is lacking is evidence of its connection with the defendant's act or omission. When the fact of control is used to justify the inference that defendant's negligence was responsible it must of course be shown that the thing in his control in fact caused the harm. In a sense, therefore, the cause of the harm must be known before the maxim can apply." H.L.A. Hart & Tony Honoré, *Causation in the Law* 419–20 (2d ed. 1985).

"Res ipsa loquitur is an appropriate form of circumstantial evidence enabling the plaintiff in particular cases to establish the defendant's likely negligence. Hence the res ipsa loquitur doctrine, properly applied, does not entail any covert form of strict liability.... The doctrine implies that the court does not know, and cannot find out, what actually happened in the individual case. Instead, the finding of likely negligence is derived from knowledge of the causes of the type or category of accidents involved." Restatement (Third) of Torts § 15 cmt. a (Discussion Draft 1999).

2. *Criminal law.* A test used to determine whether a defendant has gone beyond preparation and committed an attempt, based on whether the defendant's act itself indicated to an observer what the defendant intended to do. — Also termed (in sense 2) *equivocality.*

resisting arrest. The crime of obstructing or opposing a police officer who is making an arrest. — Also termed *resisting lawful arrest.*

resisting unlawful arrest. The act of opposing a police officer who is making an unlawful arrest. • Most jurisdictions have accepted the Model Penal Code position prohibiting the use of force to resist an unlawful arrest when the person arrested knows that a police officer is making the arrest. But some jurisdictions allow an arrestee to use nondeadly force to prevent the arrest.

res judicata (rays joo-di-**kay**-tə *or* -**kah**-tə). [Latin "a thing adjudicated"] **1.** An issue that has been definitively settled by judicial decision. **2.** An affirmative defense barring the same parties from litigating a second lawsuit on the same claim, or any other claim arising from the same transaction or series of transactions and that could have been — but was not — raised in the first suit. • The three essential elements are (1) an earlier decision on the issue, (2) a final judgment on the merits, and (3) the involvement of the same parties, or parties in privity with the original parties. Restatement (Second) of Judgments §§ 17, 24 (1982). — Also termed *res adjudicata; claim preclusion.* Cf. COLLATERAL ESTOPPEL.

" 'Res judicata' has been used in this section as a general term referring to all of the ways in which one judgment will have a binding effect on another. That usage is and doubtless will continue to be common, but it lumps under a single name two quite different effects of judgments. The first is the effect of foreclosing any litigation of matters that never have been litigated, because of the determination that they should have been advanced in an earlier suit. The second is the effect of foreclosing relitigation of matters that have once been litigated and decided. The first of these, preclusion of matters that were never litigated, has gone under the name, 'true res judicata,' or the names, 'merger' and 'bar.' The second doctrine, preclusion of matters that have once been decided, has usually been called 'collateral estoppel.' Professor Allan Vestal has long argued for the use of the names 'claim preclusion' and 'issue preclusion' for these two doctrines [Vestal, *Rationale of Preclusion*, 9 St. Louis U. L.J. 29 (1964)], and this usage is increasingly employed by the courts as it is by Restatement Second of Judgments." Charles Alan Wright, *The Law of Federal Courts* § 100A, at 722–23 (5th ed. 1994).

res litigiosae (rays li-tij-ee-**oh**-see). [Latin] *Civil law.* Things that are in litigation; property or rights that are the subject of a pending action.

res mancipi (rays **man**-sə-pI). [Latin "things of mancipium"] *Roman law.* Property that can be transferred only by a formal ceremony of mancipation. — Also termed *mancipi res; things mancipi.* See MANCIPATION.

res mobiles (rays **moh**-bə-leez). [Latin] *Civil law.* Movable things; chattels personal.

res nec mancipi (rays nek **man**-sə-pI). [Latin "things not of mancipium"] *Roman law.* Property that can be transferred without a formal ceremony of mancipation. — Also termed *things nec mancipi.*

res nova (rays **noh**-və). [Latin "new thing"] **1.** An undecided question of law. **2.** A case of first impression. — Also termed *res integra.* See *case of first impression* under CASE.

res nullius (rays nə-**lI**-əs). [Latin "thing of no one"] A thing that can belong to no one; an ownerless chattel.

Words and Phrases

Words and Phrases gives you definitions as construed by judges in case law. It is a good source to find how a word or phrase is defined in a specific factual context.

Problem

Find cases that involve the doctrine of "res ipsa loquitur," and compare how the term is defined in different contexts.

WEST'S
FEDERAL PRACTICE
DIGEST 4th

Volume 112

WORDS AND PHRASES
Pro — R

ST. PAUL, MN

WEST GROUP

REQUIREMENTS FOR LABELING OR PACKAGING

C.A.1 (Me.) 1993. Federal Insecticide, Fungicide, and Rodenticide Act (FIFRA) preempts state tort law claims based on alleged failure of manufacturer of herbicides to provide adequate warning language on products' labels, which Environmental Protection Agency (EPA) approved in accordance with FIFRA's requirements; state law liability based on such defective warning would constitute imposition by state of "requirements for labeling or packaging" under FIFRA provision prohibiting imposition of such requirements. Federal Insecticide, Fungicide, and Rodenticide Act, §§ 2–31, 24(a, b), as amended, 7 U.S.C.A. §§ 136–136y, 136v(a, b).— King v. E.I. Dupont De Nemours and Co., 996 F.2d 1346, certiorari dismissed 114 S.Ct. 490, 510 U.S. 985, 126 L.Ed.2d 440.—Agric 9.13; States 18.65.

RES

D.Nev. 1997. With respect to in rem civil forfeiture action, proceeds from federal government's sale of seized properties were nothing more than defendant "res," for purposes of calculating claimant's return-of-rents remedy for government's seizure of claimant's real property under Controlled Substances Act without affording notice and reasonable opportunity to be heard in violation of due process clause. U.S.C.A. Const.Amend. 5; Comprehensive Drug Abuse Prevention and Control Act of 1970, §§ 413(f), 511(a)(7), as amended, 21 U.S.C.A. §§ 853(f), 881(a)(7).—U.S. v. Real Property Located at Incline Village, 976 F.Supp. 1327.— Drugs & N 194.1.

RES ADJUDICATA

D.Mont. 1991. Claim preclusion, which is synonymous with "res adjudicata" as that term is used in narrow sense, bars relitigation of claim even if particular theories of recovery or defenses raised in second proceeding were not actually litigated in the first action.—Fund for Animals, Inc. v. Lujan, 794 F.Supp. 1015, affirmed 962 F.2d 1391.—Judgm 587, 619.

RES GESTAE

C.A.7 (Ind.) 1994. Under Indiana law, "res gestae" of particular offense is admissible and is defined as evidence of happenings near in time and place that complete story of crime.—Stephens v. Miller, 13 F.3d 998, certiorari denied 115 S.Ct. 57, 513 U.S. 808, 130 L.Ed.2d 15.—Crim Law 363.

C.A.10 (Kan.) 1995. Evidence of other crimes should not be suppressed when those facts come in as "res gestae," as part and parcel of proof of offense charged in indictment.—U.S. v. Kimball, 73 F.3d 269, denial of post-conviction relief affirmed 92 F.3d 1197.—Crim Law 365(1).

C.A.8 (Mo.) 1998. Under theory of "res gestae," evidence of prior crimes can be admitted when prior crime is so blended or connected with ones on trial as that proof of one incidentally involves others, explains circumstances thereof, or tends logically to prove any element of crime

charged.—U.S. v. Riebold, 135 F.3d 1226, suggestion for rehearing denied, certiorari denied 118 S.Ct. 2356, 141 L.Ed.2d 725.—Crim Law 365(2).

RES IPSA LOQUITUR

C.A.9 (Cal.) 1991. Elements which must be established to invoke doctrine of "res ipsa loquitur" are: injury-producing event of kind that ordinarily does not occur in absence of someone's negligence; event must be caused by agency or instrumentality within exclusive control of defendants; and event must not have been due to any voluntary action or contribution on part of plaintiff.—Reber v. U.S., 951 F.2d 961, certiorari denied 112 S.Ct. 1675, 503 U.S. 987, 118 L.Ed.2d 393.—Neglig 1612.

C.A.7 (Ill.) 1991. "Res ipsa loquitur" allows plaintiff to prove defendant's negligence by circumstantial evidence when direct evidence concerning cause of injury is primarily within knowledge and control of defendant.—Neace v. Laimans, 951 F.2d 139.—Neglig 1614, 1615.

C.A.7 (Ind.) 1994. "Res ipsa loquitur" is evidentiary rule which allows inference of negligence to be drawn from certain set of facts.—Newell v. Westinghouse Elec. Corp., 36 F.3d 576.—Neglig 1620.

C.A.2 (Vt.) 1993. Under Vermont law, "res ipsa loquitur" is form of circumstantial evidence that allows jury to infer from circumstances of injury that defendant has been negligent.—Connors v. University Associates In Obstetrics and Gynecology, Inc., 4 F.3d 123.—Neglig 1620.

C.A.2 (Vt.) 1993. Under Vermont law, there are four elements of "res ipsa loquitur": legal duty of defendant to exercise certain degree of care; control by defendant; causation; and requirement that event which brought on plaintiff's harm is such that it would not ordinarily occur except for want of requisite care on part of defendant as person responsible for injuring agency.—Connors v. University Associates In Obstetrics and Gynecology, Inc., 4 F.3d 123.—Neglig 1612.

C.A.10 (Wyo.) 1996. Under Wyoming law, doctrine of "res ipsa loquitur" allows trier of fact to infer negligence by defendant from circumstantial evidence when plaintiff cannot establish specific act of negligence.—Kieffer v. Weston Land, Inc., 90 F.3d 1496.—Neglig 1620.

M.D.Fla. 1997. Pursuant to doctrine of "res ipsa loquitur," happening of injury permits inference of negligence where plaintiff produces substantial evidence that injury was caused by agency or instrumentality under exclusive control and management of defendant, and that occurrence was such that in ordinary course of things occurrence would not happen if reasonable care had been used.—Ribovich v. Anheuser Busch, Inc., 972 F.Supp. 589, affirmed 180 F.3d 273.—Neglig 1613, 1614.

N.D.Ill. 1996. "Res ipsa loquitur" only applies if plaintiff can demonstrate that accident was one that does not ordinarily occur absent negligence and that the injuring instrumentality was in exclusive control of defendant.—Zarecki v. National R.R. Passenger Corp., 914 F.Supp. 1566.—Neglig 1613, 1614.

N.D.Ind. 1991. Under the doctrine of "res ipsa loquitur" inference of negligence is created by a showing that the injuring instrumentality was under the exclusive management and control of the defendant or his servants, and that in the ordinary course of things, such an accident does not occur if those with management and control use proper care; that showing shifts the burden of production to the defendant.—Amcast Indus. Corp. v. Detrex Corp., 779 F.Supp. 1519, affirmed in part, reversed in part 2 F.3d 746, certiorari denied 114 S.Ct. 691, 510 U.S. 1044, 126 L.Ed.2d 658, appeal after remand 45 F.3d 155, certiorari denied 115 S.Ct. 2248, 515 U.S. 1103, 132 L.Ed.2d 256.—Neglig 1613, 1614, 1621.

S.D.Iowa 1994. Doctrine of "res ipsa loquitur" applies, under Iowa law, when (1) injury is caused by instrumentality under exclusive control of defendant, and (2) occurrence is such as in ordinary course of things would not happen if reasonable care had been used, and if there is substantial evidence to support both elements happening of injury permits—but does not compel—inference that defendant was negligent.—Brewster v. U.S., 860 F.Supp. 1377, certified question answered 542 N.W.2d 524.—Neglig 1612.

M.D.La. 1997. Under Louisiana law, doctrine of "res ipsa loquitur" is rule of circumstantial evidence which allows court to infer defendant's negligence if facts indicate that it is more probable than not that defendant caused injury.—Hornsby v. AlliedSignal, Inc., 961 F.Supp. 923.—Neglig 1620.

E.D.Mo. 1991. "Res ipsa Loquitur" is rule of evidence permitting trier of fact to draw rebuttable inference that causes of occurrences do not ordinarily exist in absence of negligence on part of one in control.—Shaffer v. U.S., 769 F.Supp. 310.—Neglig 1620.

W.D.N.C. 1990. "Res ipsa loquitur" is an evidentiary rule that allows a party to prove negligence by establishing merely the circumstances of occurrence that produces injury, and the rule applies when plaintiff offers proof that the instrumentality causing injury was in defendant's exclusive control and that the accident was one which ordinarily does not happen in the absence of negligence.—Lindsay by Lindsay v. Public Service Co. of North Carolina, Inc., 732 F.Supp. 623, affirmed 924 F.2d 1052.—Neglig 1613, 1614.

W.D.N.C. 1990. Gas company which supplied gas to motel was not liable on the basis of "res ipsa loquitur" for guest's inhalation of carbon monoxide from defective gas-fired wall heater, where gas company did not have any control over the wall heater.—Lindsay by Lindsay v. Public Service Co. of North Carolina, Inc., 732 F.Supp. 623, affirmed 924 F.2d 1052.—Gas 20(2).

E.D.Wis. 1996. Under Wisconsin law, "res ipsa loquitur" is rule of evidence that allows negligence to be inferred in certain fact situations.—Zimbauer v. Milwaukee Orthopaedic Group, Ltd., 920 F.Supp. 959.—Neglig 1610, 1620.

RES JUDICATA

U.S.Ala. 1996. Doctrine of "res judicata" rests at bottom upon ground that party to be affected, or some other with whom he is in privity, has litigated or had opportunity to litigate same matter in former action in court of competent jurisdiction.—Richards v. Jefferson County, Ala., 116 S.Ct. 1761, 517 U.S. 793, 135 L.Ed.2d 76, on remand 682 So.2d 409, subsequent mandamus proceeding Ex parte Jefferson County, 710 So.2d 908.—Judgm 678(1), 713(2), 720.

C.A.3 1995. Under doctrine of "res judicata" or "claim preclusion," a subsequent suit based on same cause of action as a prior suit that involves same parties or their privies is barred where there has been a final judgment on merits in prior suit.—Labelle Processing Co. v. Swarrow, 72 F.3d 308, rehearing and suggestion for rehearing denied, appeal after remand 159 F.3d 1352.—Judgm 540.

C.A.5 1993. Few legal doctrines are more intrinsic or necessary in American legal system than "res judicata" doctrine, which provides that valid and final judgment precludes second suit between same parties on same claim or any part thereof, ensures that litigation will come to an end.—Medina v. I.N.S., 1 F.3d 312.—Judgm 540.

C.A.6 1994. Doctrine of "res judicata," now commonly called "claim preclusion," assures that original cause of action is extinguished by judgment, regardless of particular issues raised and litigated in the action.—Warda v. C.I.R., 15 F.3d 533, certiorari denied 115 S.Ct. 55, 513 U.S. 808, 130 L.Ed.2d 14.—Judgm 540.

C.A.11 1994. Doctrine of "res judicata" is one of finality, providing that final judgment rendered by court of competent jurisdiction on merits is conclusive as to rights and responsibilities of parties and their privies.—Baptiste v. C.I.R., 29 F.3d 1533.—Judgm 634.

C.A.Fed. 1996. "Res judicata" prevents party from relitigating same claims that were or could have been raised before.—Case, Inc. v. U.S., 88 F.3d 1004.—Judgm 713(2).

C.A.Fed. (Tex.) 1993. "Res judicata" or "claim preclusion" deals with effect of prior judgment on identical claim or cause of action between same parties.—Pfaff v. Wells Electronics, Inc., 5 F.3d 514, appeal after remand 79 F.3d 1165, order recalled and vacated 79 F.3d 1166, opinion after reinstatement of appeal 124 F.3d 1429, rehearing denied, certiorari granted in part 118 S.Ct. 1183, 140 L.Ed.2d 315, affirmed 119 S.Ct. 304, 525 U.S. 55, 142 L.Ed.2d 261, rehearing denied 119 S.Ct. 854, 142 L.Ed.2d 707, appeal after remand 124 F.3d 1429, rehearing denied, and rehearing denied, certiorari granted in part 118 S.Ct. 1183, 140 L.Ed.2d 315, affirmed 119—Judgm 634.

C.A.11 (Ala.) 1992. "Res judicata," or "claim preclusion," bars relitigation of matters that were litigated or could have been litigated in earlier

West's

FEDERAL PRACTICE
DIGEST 4th

Vol. 112

Words and Phrases
Pro — R

2000
Cumulative Annual Pocket Part

For Prior Cases Consult Federal Digest,
Modern Federal Practice Digest,
Federal Practice Digest 2d and Federal
Practice Digest 3d

ST. PAUL, MINN.

WEST GROUP

212

§ 250 comment.—In re S.N.A. Nut Co., 247 B.R. 7.—Contracts 313(2).

REQUEST FOR ACCOMMODATION

E.D.Mich. 2000. Fact that employee with cleft left hand told a union representative that she wanted a transfer to a different job because of pain in her arm was insufficient to constitute a "request for accommodation" under the ADA; union representative was not a manager or supervisor with authority to make accommodations. Americans with Disabilities Act of 1990, § 102(b)(5)(A), 42 U.S.C.A. § 12112(b)(5)(A).—Richards v. American Axle & Mfg., Inc., 84 F.Supp.2d 862.—Civil R 173.1.

E.D.Mich. 2000. Fact that employee with cleft left hand complained to her supervisor about pain in both of her arms was insufficient to constitute a "request for accommodation" for her left hand under the ADA. Americans with Disabilities Act of 1990, § 102(b)(5)(A), 42 U.S.C.A. § 12112(b)(5)(A).—Richards v. American Axle & Mfg., Inc., 84 F.Supp.2d 862.—Civil R 173.1.

REQUIRED

C.A.10 (Okla.) 2000. Sentencing guideline providing that when defendant is convicted of, inter alia, use of a firearm during a crime of violence, "the term of imprisonment is that required by statute" did not cease to apply when statute was amended to provide sentence of not less than 25 years for second conviction, though when guideline was drafted, statute mandated specific sentences, rather than a range of punishment; however, the "required" sentence is only 25 years unless defendant's criminal history category and offense level indicate a term higher than the minimum under the statute, and thus life sentence could not be imposed on defendant whose guidelines range was less than the statutory minimum. 18 U.S.C.A. § 924(c); U.S.S.G. § 2K2.4(a), 18 U.S.C.A.—U.S. v. Bazile, 209 F.3d 1205.—Sent & Pun 658; Weap 17(8).

REQUIREMENT OR PROHIBITION

C.A.2 (N.Y.) 1999. "Tombstone" provision of New York City's "Youth Protection against Tobacco Advertising and Promotion Act," which limited advertising information in restricted areas to black-and-white signs stating "TOBACCO PRODUCTS SOLD HERE," was "requirement or prohibition" within meaning of Federal Cigarette Labeling and Advertising Act's (FCLAA) preemption provision; provision was "permissive" only in literal sense that advertiser was not "required" to post tombstone sign at all. Federal Cigarette Labeling and Advertising Act, § 5(b), as amended, 15 U.S.C.A. § 1334(b); New York City Administrative Code, §§ 27–508.1 to 27–508.6.—Greater New York Metropolitan Food Council, Inc. v. Giuliani, 195 F.3d 100, certiorari denied 120 S.Ct. 1671, 146 L.Ed.2d 481.—Cons Prot 7; Mun Corp 53.

C.A.9 (Wash.) 1999. Resolution of county board of health banning outdoor tobacco advertising and requiring availability advertisements to be printed in legislatively defined tombstone format was preempted by Federal Cigarette Labeling and Advertising Act (FCLAA), because resolution imposed "requirement or prohibition" based on smoking and health with respect to cigarette advertising. Federal Cigarette Labeling and Advertising Act, § 5(b), as amended, 15 U.S.C.A. § 1334(b).—Lindsey v. Tacoma-Pierce County Health Dept., 195 F.3d 1065, opinion amended 203 F.3d 1150.—Counties 21.5; Health & E 20.

C.A.9 (Wash.) 1999. Phrase "requirement or prohibition" in provision of Federal Cigarette Labeling and Advertising Act (FCLAA) preempting any state law imposing requirement or prohibition based on smoking and health with respect to cigarette advertising encompasses positive enactments adopted by political subdivisions. Federal Cigarette Labeling and Advertising Act, § 5, as amended, 15 U.S.C.A. § 1334.—Lindsey v. Tacoma-Pierce County Health Dept., 195 F.3d 1065, opinion amended 203 F.3d 1150.—Health & E 20; Mun Corp 53.

REQUIREMENTS CONTRACT

C.A.7 (Ill.) 2000. Under Illinois law, contract for manufacture and sale of bagels was not an exclusive "requirements contract" but rather a "buyer's option"; contract did not expressly obligate buyer to purchase all, or any specified quantity, of its requirements of bagels for facility from seller, but rather contemplated use of estimates or forecasts and provided that "such forecasts shall not be binding on either party."—Brooklyn Bagel Boys, Inc. v. Earthgrains Refrigerated Dough Products, Inc., 212 F.3d 373.—Sales 71(4).

RES IPSA LOQUITUR

S.D.N.Y. 1999. "Res ipsa loquitur" is a doctrine that enables a factfinder presented only with circumstantial evidence to infer negligence simply from the fact that an event happened.—McDonough v. Celebrity Cruises, Inc., 64 F.Supp.2d 259.—Neglig 1620.

S.D.Tex. 1999. Under Texas law, doctrine of "res ipsa loquitur" is a rule of evidence, not a rule of substantive law; doctrine allows a plaintiff to show that the circumstances under which an accident or injury occurred constitute sufficient evidence of the defendant's negligence to support such a finding.—Hayles v. General Motors Corp., 82 F.Supp.2d 650.—Neglig 1610, 1619.

RES JUDICATA

C.A.Fed. (Del.) 1999. Under Texas law, "res judicata," which is also known as "claim preclusion," precludes relitigation of claims that have been finally adjudicated, or that arise out of the same subject matter and that could have been litigated in the prior action.—United Technologies Corp. v. Chromalloy Gas Turbine Corp., 189 F.3d 1338, rehearing denied, in banc suggestion declined.—Judgm 713(2), 720.

C.A.9 (Ariz.) 1999. Under the doctrine of "res judicata," a judgment on the merits in a prior suit involving the same parties or their privies bars a second suit based on the same cause of action;

6. West Reporter

West Reporter

The following pages are included to illustrate added features in many West case law reporters. They include in order:
1. Map of Federal Judicial Courts
2. Judges of the United States District Courts
3. Table of Cases reported in this volume
4. Table of Cases arranged by court subdivision
5. Words and Phrases section for cases in this volume
6. Key Number Digest for cases in this volume

West's

FEDERAL

SUPPLEMENT

Second Series
A Unit of the National Reporter System

Volume 125 F.Supp.2d

Cases Argued and Determined
in the

UNITED STATES DISTRICT COURTS

UNITED STATES COURT OF INTERNATIONAL TRADE

and Rulings of the

JUDICIAL PANEL ON MULTIDISTRICT LITIGATION

ST. PAUL, MINN.

WEST GROUP

2001

The Thirteen Federal Judicial Circuits

See 28 U.S.C.A. § 41

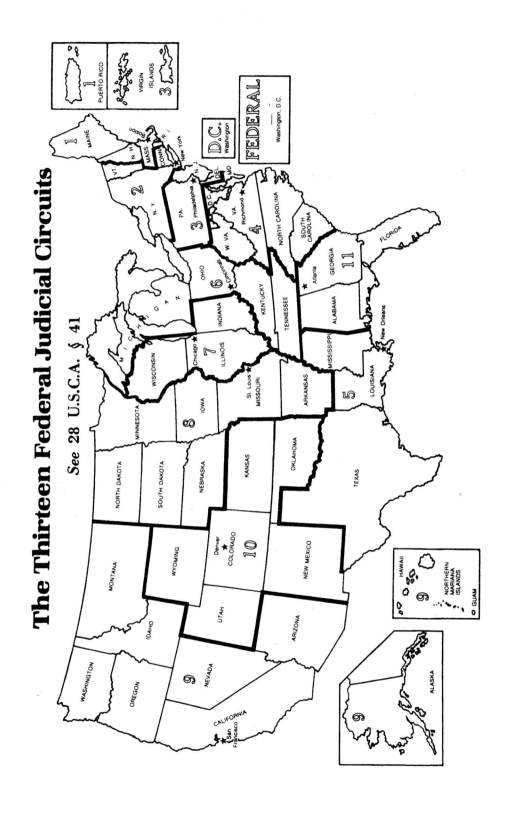

JUDGES
OF THE
UNITED STATES
DISTRICT COURTS

With Date of Appointment

DISTRICT OF COLUMBIA CIRCUIT

DISTRICT JUDGES

Norma Holloway Johnson, C.J.	5–12–80	Washington
Thomas Penfield Jackson	6–25–82	Washington
Thomas F. Hogan	10–4–82	Washington
Royce C. Lamberth	11–16–87	Washington
Paul L. Friedman	6–16–94	Washington
Gladys Kessler	6–16–94	Washington
Ricardo M. Urbina	6–16–94	Washington
Emmet G. Sullivan	6–16–94	Washington
James Robertson	10–11–94	Washington
Colleen Kollar–Kotelly	5–12–97	Washington
Henry H. Kennedy, Jr.	10–20–97	Washington
Richard W. Roberts	7–31–98	Washington
Ellen Segal Huvelle	1–12–00	Washington

SENIOR DISTRICT JUDGES

Oliver Gasch	8–11–65	Washington
William B. Bryant	8–11–65	Washington
June L. Green [1]	6–7–68	Washington
Thomas A. Flannery	12–6–71	Washington
Louis F. Oberdorfer	11–1–77	Washington
John Garrett Penn	3–23–79	Washington
Joyce Hens Green	5–11–79	Washington
Stanley S. Harris	11–11–83	Washington
Stanley Sporkin	12–17–85	Washington

FIRST CIRCUIT

DISTRICT JUDGES

D. Brock Hornby, C.J.	4–30–90	Me.	Portland
Gene Carter	6–23–83	Me.	Portland
George Z. Singal	7–17–00	Me.	Bangor
William G. Young, C.J.	4–4–85	Mass.	Boston
Joseph L. Tauro	10–17–72	Mass.	Boston

---

1. Deceased February 2, 2001

VII

CASES REPORTED

XXIX

CASES REPORTED

ARRANGED UNDER THEIR RESPECTIVE CIRCUITS

XXXV

WORDS AND PHRASES

For other judicial definitions,
see publication WORDS AND PHRASES.

AD INTERIM STIPULATION,
In re American Milling Co., Unlimited, E.D.Mo., 125 F.Supp.2d 981.

ADMINISTRATIVE REMEDY,
Concepcion v. Morton, D.N.J., 125 F.Supp.2d 111.

ADVERSE EMPLOYMENT ACTION,
Gasser v. Ramsey, D.D.C., 125 F.Supp.2d 1.

ADVERSE PERSONNEL ACTION,
Roberts v. Segal Company, D.D.C., 125 F.Supp.2d 545.

ARTFUL PLEADING DOCTRINE,
Minnesota ex rel. Hatch v. Worldcom, Inc., D.Minn., 125 F.Supp.2d 365.

ASSOCIATION,
Moongate Water Co., Inc. v. Butterfield Park Mutual Domestic Water Ass'n., D.N.M., 125 F.Supp.2d 1304.

CLEARLY ESTABLISHED,
Morris v. Wallace Community College-Selma, S.D.Ala., 125 F.Supp.2d 1315.

CLEARLY ESTABLISHED LAW,
Morris v. Wallace Community College-Selma, S.D.Ala., 125 F.Supp.2d 1315.

CLOTHES,
Bejil v. Ethicon, Inc., N.D.Tex., 125 F.Supp.2d 192.

CLOTHING,
Bejil v. Ethicon, Inc., N.D.Tex., 125 F.Supp.2d 192.

COMPLETE PREEMPTION,
Minnesota ex rel. Hatch v. Worldcom, Inc., D.Minn., 125 F.Supp.2d 365.

CONSTRUCTIVE DISCHARGE,
Maluo v. Nakano, D.Hawai'i, 125 F.Supp.2d 1224.

CONTINUING VIOLATION,
Morris v. Wallace Community College-Selma, S.D.Ala., 125 F.Supp.2d 1315.
Maluo v. Nakano, D.Hawai'i, 125 F.Supp.2d 1224.

CONTINUING VIOLATION DOCTRINE,
Maluo v. Nakano, D.Hawai'i, 125 F.Supp.2d 1224.

CONVERSION,
Special Purpose Accounts Receivable Co-op Corp. v. Prime One Capital Co., S.D.Fla., 125 F.Supp.2d 1093.

COST ITEM,
University of Hawaii Professional Assembly v. Cayetano, D.Hawai'i, 125 F.Supp.2d 1237.

CULMINATED,
Jaudon v. Elder Health, Inc., D.Md., 125 F.Supp.2d 153.

CUSTOMERS,
Investors Capital Corp. v. Brown, M.D.Fla., 125 F.Supp.2d 1346.

DIRECT EVIDENCE,
Preston v. Berendsen Fluid Power, W.D.Mich., 125 F.Supp.2d 245.

DISABILITY,
Gasser v. Ramsey, D.D.C., 125 F.Supp.2d 1.

DISCRETIONARY AUTHORITY,
Morris v. Wallace Community College-Selma, S.D.Ala., 125 F.Supp.2d 1315.

Neal F. GASSER, Plaintiff,

v.

Charles H. RAMSEY, Defendant.

Civil Action No. 00–534 (GK).

United States District Court,
District of Columbia.

Oct. 10, 2000.

Police officer brought action alleging
that his involuntary transfer to desk job
because of blood thinning condition caused
by prescription medication violated Americans with Disabilities Act (ADA). On employer's motion for judgment on the plead-
ings, the District Court, Kessler, J., held
that: (1) officer had "disability"; (2) officer
was substantially limited from performing
broad class of jobs; and (3) officer's involuntary transfer constituted "adverse employment action."

Motion denied.

1. Civil Rights ☞173.1

Police officer whose blood did not
properly clot because of prescription medication he took to alleviate his Protein S
deficiency had "disability" for purposes of
ADA, where officer's blood thinning condition caused him to be involuntarily transferred to desk job. Americans with Disabilities Act of 1990, § 3(2)(A), 42 U.S.C.A.
§ 12102(2)(A).

> See publication Words and Phras-
> es for other judicial constructions
> and definitions.

2. Civil Rights ☞173.1

Police officer whose blood did not
properly clot because of prescription medication he took to alleviate his Protein S
deficiency was substantially limited from
performing broad class of jobs, for purposes of ADA, as result of his condition,

where officer's blood thinning condition
caused him to be involuntarily transferred
to desk job, despite fact that his job did
not subject him to significantly different
type of trauma than that faced by large
numbers of employees in course of different lines of employment. Americans with
Disabilities Act of 1990, § 3(2)(C), 42
U.S.C.A. § 12102(2)(C); 29 C.F.R.
§ 1630.2.

3. Civil Rights ☞173.1

District of Columbia's involuntary
transfer of police sergeant to desk job
rendered him ineligible for up to $20,000
per year in overtime pay, and cost him
promotional opportunity, and thus constituted "adverse employment action" sufficient to support officer's ADA action.
Americans with Disabilities Act of 1990,
§ 102(a), 42 U.S.C.A. § 12112(a).

> See publication Words and Phras-
> es for other judicial constructions
> and definitions.

———————

Michael P. Deeds, James L. Kestell,
Kestell and Associates, Falls Church, VA,
for plaintiff.

Robert A. DeBerardinis, Jr., E. Louise
R. Phillips, Office of Corporation Counsel,
Office of the Administrator, Washington,
DC, for defendant.

MEMORANDUM OPINION

KESSLER, District Judge.

I. Introduction

Plaintiff Neal F. Gasser, a District of
Columbia police officer, brings suit against
his employer under the Americans with
Disabilities Act, 42 U.S.C. § 12101 et seq.
("ADA"), and Section 501 of the Rehabilitation Act of 1973, as amended, 29 U.S.C.
§ 791 et seq.[1] Plaintiff alleges that Defendant has discriminated against him on the

---

1. The parties do not argue, and the case law
does not indicate, that the relevant analytical
or legal questions depend on whether Plaintiff's cause of action is brought under the ADA

or the Rehabilitation Act. See, e.g., Daugherty
v. City of El Paso, 56 F.3d 695, 697–98 (5th
Cir.1995). Therefore, this Opinion simply refers to the ADA.

7. Westlaw

Westlaw

Westlaw is a computer-based legal research tool. It draws from the West database of legal information, allowing you to quickly find relevant case material. Using Westlaw allows you to receive the most current information possible. For example, U.S. Supreme Court opinions are usually available within 30 minutes of their release. Westlaw also gives you access to KeyCite, an up-to-date citation research service.

The following pages provide a brief overview of how to navigate through Westlaw.

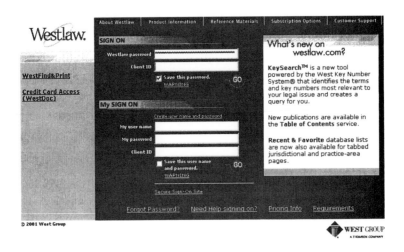

This is the Sign On Westlaw® page. Enter your Westlaw password and client ID here to begin your research.

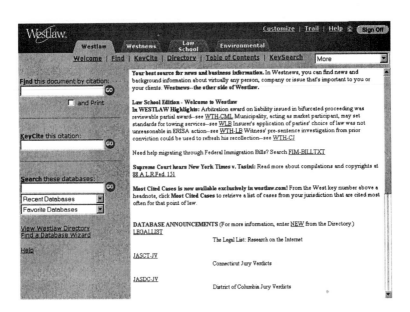

This is the tabbed Westlaw page. From this page you can access all the resources available on Westlaw.

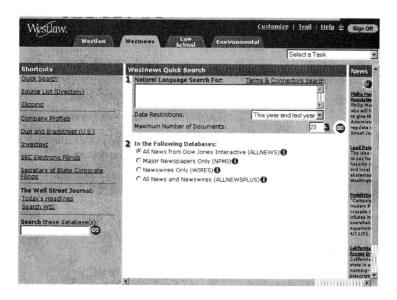

This is the tabbed Westnews™ page. This page is a starting point for research focused on news and business information. The left frame of the page provides links to the Westnews section of the Westlaw Directory, the WestClip™ clipping service, databases containing company information, and The Wall Street Journal database.

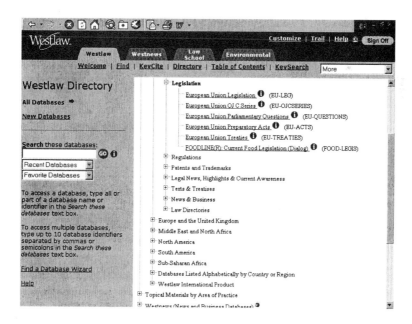

This is the Westlaw Directory page, which lists the more than 15,000 databases and services on Westlaw, including Westnews. You can access the Westlaw Directory from any page on Westlaw by clicking **Directory** on the toolbar. Clicking the plus and minus symbols expands and collapses a category of databases. A blue link indicates a searchable database. Click a database name to access the database.

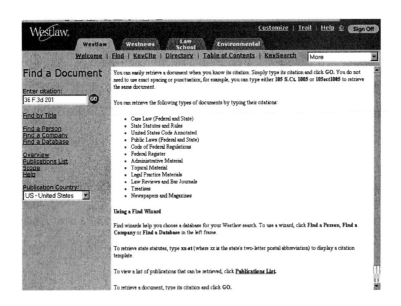

This is the Find a Document page. You can use the Find service to retrieve many types of documents, including case law, statutes, regulations, and law review articles, for which you know the citations. You can access Find from the tabbed Westlaw page or from any page on Westlaw by clicking **Find** on the toolbar.

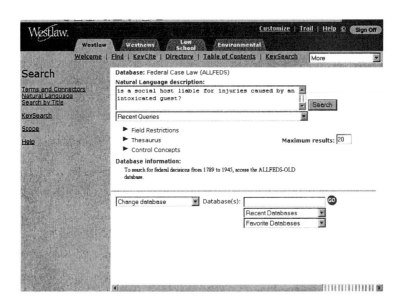

This is the Search page with the Natural Language search method selected. Natural Language searching allows you to use plain English to retrieve relevant documents.

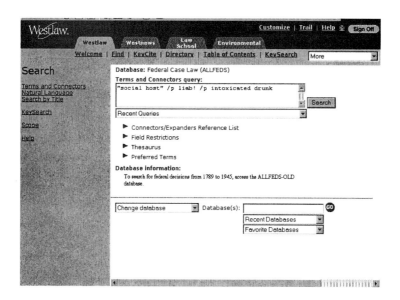

This is the Search page with the Terms and Connectors search method selected. Key terms are joined by connectors that specify the relationship between those terms (in the example above, "/p" means within the same paragraph, and the space between *intoxicated* and *drunk* means "or").

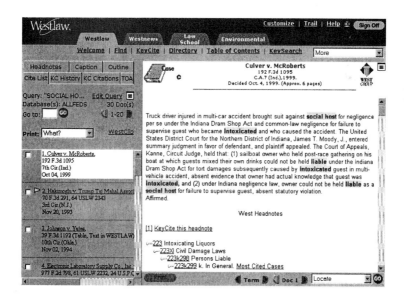

This is a search result from a case law database, shown in split-page view. The case is displayed in the right frame. You can access relevant information about this case using the tabs in the left frame. A full-page view of the case is also available.

This full-page search result shows search terms highlighted in yellow. The *Term* arrows at the bottom of the page allow you to move forward to the next highlighted term or backward to the previous highlighted term.

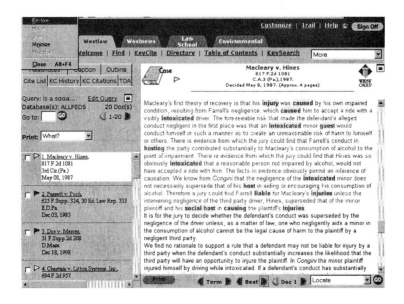

This page shows a Natural Language search result. You can browse the documents using the *Term* arrows to go to the terms used in your search or using the *Best* arrows to move to the portion of the document that most closely matches your search terms. The "best" portion is displayed in red text.

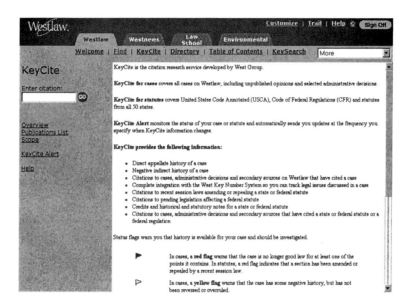

This is the KeyCite® page. KeyCite is the citation research service available exclusively on Westlaw that helps you quickly determine whether a case or statute is good law and retrieve citing references. You can access KeyCite from the tabbed Westlaw page or from any page by clicking **KeyCite** on the toolbar.

You can also access KeyCite from a displayed case or statute by clicking the KeyCite status flag in the document header or by clicking the **KC History** or **KC Citations** tab in the left frame.

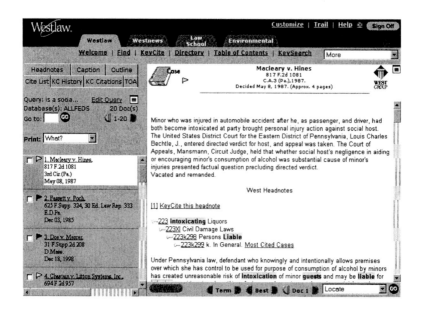

The red and yellow flags in the upper-left corner of the case and in the citations list in the left frame are part of the KeyCite service on Westlaw. A red flag warns that the case is no longer good law for at least one of the points it contains. A yellow flag warns that the case has some negative history but has not been reversed or overruled.

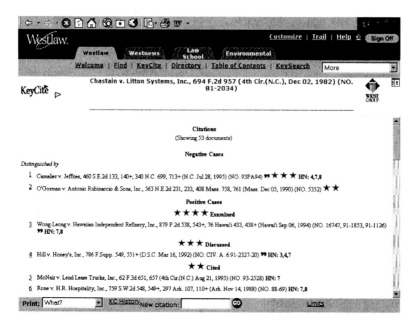

This is a full-page view of the KC Citations tab. KeyCite depth of treatment stars indicate the extent to which a citing case discusses the cited case. Quotation marks indicate that the citing case directly quotes the cited case. Headnote numbers indicate the issues for which the cited case was cited.

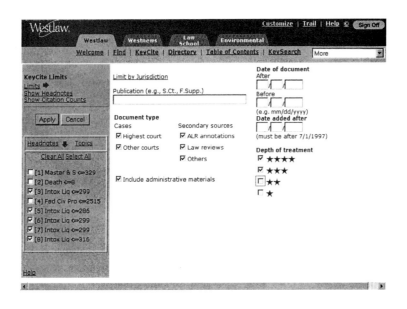

The KeyCite Limits page allows you to limit citing references to specific issue(s), jurisdiction(s), depth of treatment, date, document type(s), or any combination of these.

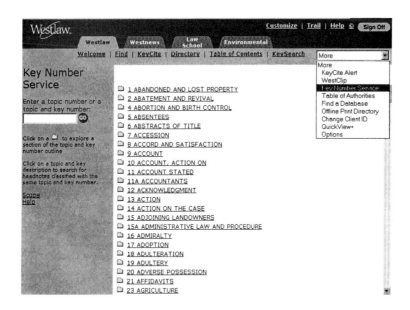

This is the Key Number Service page. The Key Number Service provides on outline of West digest topics and key numbers in their hierarchical context. You can access the Key Number Service from the drop-down list on the toolbar or from the link from the topic and key number in a case headnote.

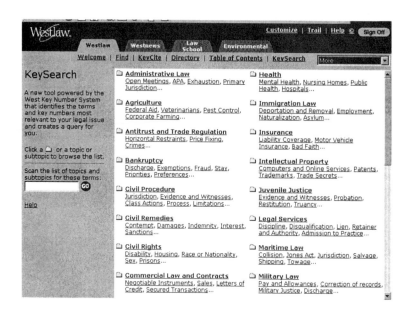

The KeySearch™ service helps you find cases and secondary sources within a specific area of the law by creating a Terms and Connectors query. You can access KeySearch by clicking **KeySearch** on the toolbar.

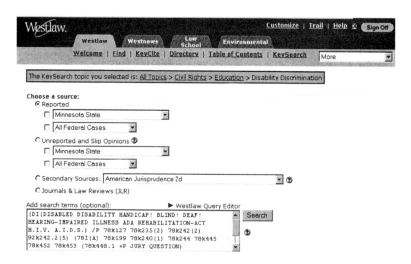

This page shows the KeySearch query. KeySearch uses the key numbers and their underlying concepts to retrieve both cases that contain the key numbers and documents that do not contain key numbers, such as unpublished cases and secondary sources.

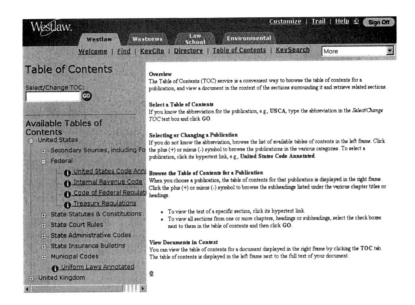

This is the Table of Contents page. The Table of Contents service allows you to view a document in the context of the sections surrounding it and to retrieve related sections. You can access the Table of Contents service by clicking **Table of Contents** on the toolbar.

You can also access the Table of Contents service from the TOC tab in the left frame when viewing a statute or regulation in the right frame.

8. Hornbooks

Hornbooks

The Hornbook is a one-volume treatise on a specific area of law. In this example, the area of law is TORTS.

The enclosed sample pages include a discussion on negligent infliction of emotional harm, with a look at the general rules of liability for the same. Editions of Hornbooks also include Westlaw references with suggested queries for research.

THE LAW OF TORTS

By

Dan B. Dobbs

Professor of Law
The University of Arizona
James E. Rogers College of Law

HORNBOOK SERIES®

WEST
GROUP

ST. PAUL, MINN., 2000

actions, and consequently a therapist who seduces his patient has no obligation to the patient's spouse and is not liable for the spouse's emotional injury when the seduction is discovered.[6] But when both spouses are patients of the therapist, the therapist's seduction of one may be an intentional or reckless infliction of distress upon the other in the light of the therapists undertaking to care for both.[7] Possibly also, a therapist who implants in his patient the false belief that her father sexually abused her may be liable for the parent's emotional distress at losing his child's affections.[8]

Bodily harm resulting. When emotional harm is inflicted by conduct "directed at" the plaintiff, the Restatement requires proof of severe emotional harm but does not require any bodily injury resulting from the emotions. When the defendant "directs" his acts at another person, however, the Restatement requires the non-family plaintiff to prove not only the distress but resulting bodily harm. The rule seems to have been adopted from the negligence cases, presumably because the American Law Institute believed that emotional harm to third persons would be less likely or less severe and that bodily harm would guarantee the reality or the extent of the emotional harm. Neither proposition seems necessarily so. A woman who watches deliberate injury to or murder of her husband is likely enough to be distressed. Proof of a resulting rash adds nothing to the reality or the extent of the injury. Such a requirement is being rejected by some courts even in negligent infliction cases,[9] and probably should be discarded in these third person cases as well.

TOPIC C.　NEGLIGENT INFLICTION OF EMOTIONAL HARM

§ 308.　General Rules of Liability for Negligent Infliction of Emotional Harm

Original rule denying recovery. As already indicated, damages for emotional distress are recoverable in connection with many torts, includ-

6. Homer v. Long, 90 Md.App. 1, 599 A.2d 1193 (1992).

7. See Horak v. Biris, 130 Ill.App.3d 140, 474 N.E.2d 13, 85 Ill.Dec. 599 (1985); Rowe v. Bennett, 514 A.2d 802 (Me.1986); cf. Destefano v. Grabrian, 763 P.2d 275 (Colo.1988) (clergy person providing marriage counseling to both spouses and who has sexual intercourse with one of them is liable to the other for outrageous infliction of distress). Something similar has applied in negligence cases. See Marlene F. v. Affiliated Psychiatric Med. Clinic, Inc., 48 Cal.3d 583, 770 P.2d 278, 257 Cal.Rptr. 98 (1989) (therapist treating both mother and son liable to mother for molestation of son); cf. Christensen v. Superior Court (Pasadena Crematorium of Altadena), 54 Cal.3d 868, 820 P.2d 181, 2 Cal.Rptr.2d 79 (1991) (neg-ligent infliction of distress in light of contractual relationship to treat dead body properly, but, paradoxically, no intentional infliction claim since plaintiffs were not present).

8. See Joel Jay Finer, Therapists' Liability to the Falsely Accused for Inducing Illusory Memories of Childhood Sexual Abuse—Current Remedies and a Proposed Statute, 11 J. L. & HEALTH 45 (1996–97) (suggesting liability when therapist creates substantial risks of engendering false memories and false accusations); see § 443.

9. See Molien v. Kaiser Found. Hosps., 27 Cal.3d 916, 167 Cal.Rptr. 831, 616 P.2d 813, 16 A.L.R. 4th 518 (1980), modified, Burgess v. Superior Court, 2 Cal.4th 1064, 831 P.2d 1197, 9 Cal.Rptr.2d 615 (1992).

ing ordinary personal injury cases.[1] When the defendant's negligent act caused emotional distress alone, without causing personal injury, courts at one time simply denied all recovery unless the defendant's act amounted to some other tort such as libel or slander.[2] They tended to think of the emotional harm claim as one for fright or shock, a characterization that still seems to shape some of the rules.[3]

Rationale for denial. Reasons for the complete denial of emotional distress recoveries have tended to sound less persuasive over the years. Lawyers argued that the emotional harm was simply not cognizable in courts of law, that it was not a proximate result of the defendant's negligent act, that it could not be measured in dollars, that it might not be real, and that fraudulent or exaggerated claims might proliferate. These reasons counsel nothing more than the usual trial to determine the reality and extent of the claim and the usual judicial control over excessive verdicts; they do not support an absolute rule against recovery for emotional distress. Consequently, courts today recognize many cases for recovery even while they impose many constraints.

Contemporary allowance of the claim for negligent infliction of distress. When the defendant was negligent and emotional harm was foreseeable and caused in fact by his negligence, most courts today do allow many recoveries for stand-alone emotional harm.[4] At the same time, they remain deeply concerned to impose a limit. Many courts impose special limitations when the plaintiff's distress results from harm to another person.[5] They may correspondingly relax the special demands when the defendant has assumed a duty to the plaintiff or one is imposed by law because of the relationship between the plaintiff and defendant.[6]

These cases aside, most courts hold that the plaintiff can recover only if a normally constituted person would suffer,[7] and the plaintiff in fact suffered severe distress.[8] In addition, they adopt one of the additional restrictions stated below.

1. *Telegraphic death messages and dead bodies. The plaintiff can recover for distress arising only where the defendant negligently transmits or fails to deliver telegraphic messages (wrongly an-*

---

§ 308

1. § 302.

2. Some of the many articles discussing the rule, usually criticizing it, are listed in § 302.

3. See § 311.

4. Texas insists that the claim for negligent infliction of distress may proceed only if there is a tort to someone, so it may allow the claim of a bystander who witnesses a tort to someone else, but not a claim for distress inflicted more directly. See Boyles v. Kerr, 855 S.W.2d 593 (Tex.1993).

5. § 309.

6. See § 312.

7. See § 313.

8. Bovsun v. Sanperi, 61 N.Y.2d 219, 461 N.E.2d 843, 473 N.Y.S.2d 357 (1984); Johnson v. Ruark Obstetrics and Gynecology Assocs., P.A., 327 N.C. 283, 304, 395 S.E.2d 85, 97 (1990) ("the term 'severe emotional distress' means any emotional or mental disorder, such as, for example, neurosis, psychosis, chronic depression, phobia, or any other type of severe and disabling emotional or mental condition which may be generally recognized and diagnosed by professionals trained to do so"); Heldreth v. Marrs, 188 W.Va. 481, 425 S.E.2d 157 (1992).

Nutshells

Nutshells are compact study guides that give a brief, concise overview of a very specific area of law.

The enclosed pages from the Criminal Law Nutshell look at causation in relation to homicide. Nutshells also include research references and a table of cases.

CRIMINAL LAW

IN A NUTSHELL

THIRD EDITION

By

ARNOLD H. LOEWY
Professor of Law
University of North Carolina

WEST
GROUP

ST. PAUL, MINN.
2000

ly, a defendant who knows that he is creating an unreasonable risk of death to his passenger by driving 90 miles per hour in a 50 mile per hour zone is guilty of at least involuntary manslaughter if his passenger dies instantly in a crash attributable to his excessive speed. Unfortunately, not all cases are so clear. Many times a death is attributable to more than one cause. In such a case, a court must determine whether the manner of death is sufficiently related to the defendant's conduct that the death can be fairly attributed to him. When a court concludes that the death is fairly attributable to the defendant's conduct, it uses the term "proximately caused" to describe that conclusion. *E.g.,* Stephenson v. S., 179 N.E. 633 (Ind.1932). Because the defendant's conduct is a factor in questions of causation, we will consider intentional killings separate from unintentional killings. The causation problems in felony murder and misdemeanor manslaughter cases have been considered elsewhere (§§ 2.09, 2.10 *supra*) and will not be considered in this chapter.

§ 3.02 Intentional Killings

At a minimum, the state must prove simple "but for" causation, *i.e.,* "but for" defendant's act, the victim would not have died at the time and in the manner that he did. One exception to this rule is when two forces simultaneously inflict an injury, each of which, standing alone, would have been instantly fatal. In this situation, it is not true that "but for" defendant's act, the victim would have lived longer than he did. Nevertheless, an intentional act which produces such a result is deemed to be a cause of death.

Although proof of "but for" causation is essential to establish liability, it is not, standing alone, sufficient to establish proximate cause. The real question in determining proximate cause is the extent to which it is justifiable to hold a defendant liable for a death occurring in an unanticipated manner. As an illustration, suppose a defendant shoots at a potential victim intending to kill him but in fact misses. The victim then enters a building (which he otherwise would not have entered) in order to avoid being shot. As he enters, the building explodes (because of a bomb put there by a third person) thereby killing the victim. In such a case the original defendant would not be guilty of murder even though the victim would not have been killed "but for" the original shooting. Unfortunately, the result in other situations is not this clear. When a defendant intends to cause death (or to a lesser extent when she intends to inflict serious injury), the courts tend to hold her liable for the ultimate death unless there is a very clear break in the causal link. For example, A shoots at B intending to kill him, but misses. B, who unbeknown to A had a weak heart, dies of a heart attack. Assuming that "but for" the shot B would not have died of a heart attack at that time, A will be guilty of murder. *Cf.* S. v. Luther, 206 S.E.2d 238 (N.C.1974). Defendant, who intended to kill the victim, was guilty of murder even if the victim's death resulted from the conjunction of the victim's heart disease with the excitement and shock of defendant's assault.

Cases involving intervening causes are somewhat more difficult. When A shoots B, leaving her to die and C comes along and stabs B thereby hastening her death, it is clear that C is guilty of murder (intentionally shortening the life of another). Nevertheless, most courts would also hold A liable, on the ground that at the time of death both wounds were contributing to the life shortening process. If C had decapitated B, it would be harder to hold A responsible for the resulting death. See S. v. Luster, 182 S.E. 427 (S.C.1935). Most likely, C's supervening act would limit A's liability to attempted murder. Even here, however, A might be held liable on the ground that his intent to kill B rendered B unable to defend herself against C, thereby proximately causing her death. *Cf.* Henderson v. Kibbe, 431 U.S. 145 (1977). (Defendants guilty of second degree murder when, after robbing a thoroughly intoxicated man and abandoning him on an unlighted road on a cold night, the man was hit by a truck and killed.)

The "negligent treatment of a wound" cases present substantially the same problem. When A seriously wounds B in an attempt to kill him and B dies from negligent medical treatment, A is guilty of murder. Hall v. S., 159 N.E. 420 (Ind.1928). If the treatment is outrageously negligent, however, and it is clear that the treatment is the primary cause of death, there is some authority holding the defendant not guilty of murder. *E.g.,* R. v. Jordan, 40 Crim.App. 152 (1956).

Another category of case where courts frequently find liability is where the victim in some manner contributes to her own death after the defendant's attack. When the attack was still contributing to the victim's death, courts don't care if the victim's own lack of desire to live contributes to her death. D is still liable. P. v. Brackett, 510 N.E.2d 877 (Ill.1987). Even when the death was a suicide, if it can be fairly said that D drove V to it, courts tend to impose liability. Stephenson v. S., 179 N.E. 633 (Ind.1932).

Obviously, these examples can be multiplied (and doubtless most criminal law professors will do precisely that), but in a book this size, these examples should suffice to demonstrate the bias in favor of homicidal liability for deaths which would not have occurred ''but for'' the defendant's intentional act.

§ 3.03 Unintentional Killings

Courts seem less willing to attribute a victim's death to defendant's wrongful conduct when the defendant does not intend to kill. When the defendant intends to inflict serious injury, but in fact causes death, there not likely to be a great distinction made in causation terms from an intent to kill case that results in death. When the defendant intends no harm, however, but is merely reckless, grossly negligent, or ordinarily negligent, there is a tendency to carefully scrutinize the circumstances of the death before concluding that they are fairly attributable to the defendant's wrongful conduct.

A good illustration is a modified version of one of the situations presented in § 3.02 *supra*. Assume that A is driving his automobile at 90 miles per hour in a 50 mile per hour zone, and B, his passenger, who unbeknown to A has a weak heart, dies of a heart attack brought on by the fear of an accident which never transpires. Unless A should have reasonably foreseen that his culpably negligent driving would cause a heart attack, a persuasive argument can be made that he should not be guilty of manslaughter. See S. v. Hall, 299 S.E.2d 680 (N.C.App. 1983) (to find proximate cause in a homicide case, one must find that a person of ordinary prudence could have reasonably foreseen that such a result, or some similar injurious result, was *probable* under the facts as they existed).

Of course, this is contrary to the situation in which the killing was intentional, *e.g.* the shooting illustration in § 3.02 *supra*. Nevertheless, since the purpose of criminal law is punishment rather than compensation (§ 1.01 *supra*), there is some reluctance on the part of courts to hold a defendant criminally liable for an unintended and unanticipated death. Some courts, however, have carried this reluctance to an extreme. For example, in C. v. Root, 170 A.2d 310 (Pa.1961), the court exculpated a defendant automobile highway racer from liability for the death of his opponent occasioned by the opponent's attempt to pass in a highly dangerous manner. The court reasoned that the opponent's reckless act was a sufficiently superceding cause of death that the defendant's original conduct in entering the race was not a substantial factor in producing death. Its opinion emphasized that it was requiring a stricter standard of proximate cause than it would require in a tort case.

Some courts reject *Root* reasoning and would impose liability in that kind of a situation. See S. v. McFadden, 320 N.W.2d 608 (Iowa 1982). Where the defendant's behavior is outrageously reckless, causation principles are arguably closer to intentional killing. (See P. v. Russell, 693 N.E.2d 193 (N.Y. 1998) where the court imposed murder liability on all participants in a gun battle, even though it was unclear which side fired the fatal bullet that killed a passerby.)

§ 3.04   Year and a Day Rule

At common law, death could not be attributed to defendant's wrongful conduct unless it occurred within a year and a day of the conduct. The rationale for this rule was the lack of medical precision in determining cause after such a long period of time, coupled with the very real probability of an intervening cause being responsible for the death. In view of the medical advances of the twentieth century, it can be argued that the year and a day rule is obsolete and should be discarded. Although some jurisdictions have done this either by legislation or judicial decision, most jurisdictions have not. See Elliott v. Mills, 335 P.2d 1104 (Okl.Cr.App. 1959).

Notes

Notes